'Is that any wa
husband?'

'As far as I'm concerned you're no longer my husband,' Sapphire told him coldly. 'Leaving you was the best thing I ever did.'

'You enjoy living by yourself?' He sat down, looking as if he was prepared to stay for a long time.

She nodded, though it was a lie. Apart from her photography her life was empty. She missed Drake more than she liked to admit.

Dear Reader

Who are your favourite Mills & Boon heroes? We'll bet our bottom *ecu* that European men—French, Greek and Italian—will be among them. There's something unique about courtship Continental-style! Which is why Mills & Boon has launched *Euromance*—a book each month that features a gorgeous hero from one of the twelve EC countries. This month you can experience the sensual charm of the Irish, in Emma Richmond's gentle tale, LOVE OF MY HEART—look out for the attractive paperback cover!

The Editor

Margaret Mayo was born in the industrial Midlands and began writing fifteen years ago after getting an idea for a romantic short story. It turned into a full-scale novel and she now has over forty novels to her credit. She lives with her husband in a pretty village in Staffordshire and has a grown-up son and daughter. She enjoys setting her books both at home and in exotic locations which she either visits or researches through books from the library.

YESTERDAY'S DREAMS

BY

MARGARET MAYO

MILLS & BOON LIMITED
ETON HOUSE 18-24 PARADISE ROAD
RICHMOND SURREY TW9 1SR

First published in Great Britain 1993
by Mills & Boon Limited

This edition 1993

ISBN 0 263 78013 9

Set in Times Roman 10 on 11½ pt.
01-9305-55703 C

Made and printed in Great Britain

CHAPTER ONE

SAPPHIRE was so deep in thought that she did not hear the car pull up behind hers, or footsteps approach. She knew nothing until her door was wrenched open and a withering voice said, 'I wondered how long it would take you to come back.'

Her head jerked on her shoulders as she twisted round to look up at the man she had lived with for two bitter-sweet years, and her heart began to beat like a sledge-hammer within her breast. It came as a shock to discover that she was still not immune to Drake, that he still had the power to melt her bones, set every limb trembling.

'I've not come back,' she told him coolly, but there was a huskiness to her voice that caught her by surprise. She cleared her throat and said more firmly, 'I happened to be passing, that's all.'

His face looked thinner than she remembered, much gaunter, though no less striking; his strong features were harshly arrogant, his square jaw grim and determined, his mouth inflexible yet still with a hint of sensuality—and his raw, animal vitality had in no way diminished.

'Passing?' Thick brows rose disbelievingly. Treetops was well off the beaten track.

'OK, so I made a slight detour, but I was in the area and——'

'And you thought you'd drop in on me? A social visit, no less. How charming.' The bitter, disbelieving edge to his voice sent a cold shiver down Sapphire's spine. There was no smile after all these months, no hint of pleasure, nothing except cold hostility.

'I had no intention of calling on you,' she said defensively. It was pure chance that had brought her to this part of Cornwall, but once here she had not been able to leave without stopping to look at the house they had once shared. She had not been afraid that she might bump into him, not afraid in the least. He was never home in the middle of the day.

'So what was it, morbid curiosity to see whether anything had changed? Are you missing the life of luxury you turned your back on?'

'Why would I miss an empty life?' she snapped. 'I don't know what prompted me, but you can rest assured that if I'd known you were here wild horses wouldn't have dragged me within ten miles.' She had been full of dreams and plans when she married Drake Rivelin and moved into Treetops, his delightfully converted farmhouse home near Launceston. But her happiness had not lasted. Perhaps she ought to have known in the beginning, ought to have guessed from his lifestyle that he would not spend much time at home. Perhaps she had wanted more from him then he was prepared to give.

His light blue eyes hardened in sudden anger. 'We need to talk, Sapphire. I want to know what made you walk out on me without so much as a word.'

She shook her head emphatically. 'It would serve no purpose.'

'I happen to think differently,' he rasped. 'Get out of your car—we're going into the house.' His hand shot out to grasp her wrist, and Sapphire knew he was capable of manhandling her indoors if she dared to resist.

She had never seen him look so savagely determined, but it was still with great reluctance that she accompanied him down the winding driveway and into the house, and as she followed him into the sitting-room at the back, the room with the spectacular view over the valley, she felt every nerve go as taut as a bowstring.

She could smell his familiar masculine scent, feel the remembered warmth of his body as she moved past him, and she had to check the urge to halt and touch her hands to his face, to raise her lips to his for a kiss so exciting that it threatened to send her spinning into space. It had always been like this, and surprisingly nothing had changed.

It was this room, filled, like the rest of the house, with beautiful pieces of furniture—antique and modern blending happily together, where she had sat for hour after long hour waiting, always waiting, and then in the end the quarrels, the unending arguments, and finally the galling discovery that Drake was being unfaithful to her, that it was probably his affair with another woman that kept him away from home and not the pressure of work as he had led her to believe. It was the final insult, and she had packed her bags and walked out. That was six months ago, six long, agonising months, and she had not heard from him since.

Sapphire stood at the window with her back to the room, tall, unconsciously graceful, her shoulder-length auburn hair glossy and thick, the simple ivory suit screaming understated elegance.

'Tea, Sapphire? Coffee?'

'No, thanks, nothing.' She listened to the sound of her heart drumming a tattoo within her breast. Before she saw Drake again she had thought her feelings dead; now she knew they were very much alive and in definite danger of threatening her sanity.

'I suggest you sit down.'

The brusque tone of his voice made her spin around to face him, her beautiful navy eyes, wide-spaced and thickly lashed, uneasy as they saw the cool rejection in his much lighter ones. Whatever she had imagined when meeting Drake again, it was not this open animosity.

She had never dreamt that he would be so coldly distant. He must know why she had left him; surely he didn't think she would sit back and accept his infidelity? Unless his secretary had said nothing and he did not know she had found out? Maybe Hélène had kept quiet because she feared she might lose her job if he knew she had told his wife he was away and she had therefore realised he was with another woman?

Unwillingly Sapphire lowered herself on to one of the rose-coloured, well-padded chairs; Drake followed suit, his eyes never leaving her heart-shaped face. She wondered whether he thought she was going to beg him to take her back, whether he thought that was the reason she was here. How little he knew her if he did—it was the last thing she would do. Maybe she still loved him, she wasn't sure exactly what she felt at this moment, but she certainly had no intention of going down on her knees and saying she wanted to come home. And judging by the implacable hardness on his face, he didn't want her back either. The thought, surprisingly, hurt.

'Where have you been hiding yourself this last six months?' There was a rough edge to his voice that grated over her skin like sandpaper and sent an uncontrollable shiver down her spine.

Sapphire lifted her chin determinedly. 'I think that's my business.'

'In other words, you don't want me to know where you're living? Was I such an ogre, Sapphire, that you had to walk out on me?'

'Not an ogre,' she tossed back, 'but your work means so much to you that I doubt you've even missed me. It was quite a surprise seeing you here today.'

'I always told you it wouldn't last, that there would come a time when I wouldn't work such long hours.'

'And that time has come? Is that what you're saying?' She held her breath as she waited for his answer.

'Not exactly,' Drake admitted.

Sapphire's brief spurt of hope faded. 'In that case, you should know why I walked out,' she retorted sharply. Let him think it was solely because of his work. It was the major factor, in any case. She had thought of leaving him long before she discovered that he was two-timing her.

'And now you're back because you're short of money!' he barked. 'You thought you'd try to bleed me for a little more.'

His sudden, unreasonable accusation took Sapphire by surprise, and she looked at him, stunned. 'What on earth are you talking about?'

'Now I've stopped your allowance you're finding it hard to make ends meet, isn't that it?' he sneered. 'You'd got used to the life of luxury. You can't buy any more pretty new clothes?'

'You're out of your mind!' she slung at him savagely, unable to accept that he thought so badly of her.

'Am I? I don't think so.' He cast a disparaging glance at her cream suit. 'Very elegant, but there'll be no more like that, I can assure you—not at my expense.

Sapphire was furious. 'You think I'm after your money? My God, Drake, I never realised your opinion of me was so low. If I'd known I'd never have let you drag me in here, that's a fact; all we're doing is wasting each other's time.' She walked across to the door, her chin high, her eyes spitting fire. 'Don't bother to see me out, I know my own way.' It was with a sense of satisfaction that she slammed the door resoundingly behind her.

* * *

Sapphire had been born and brought up in Devizes in Wiltshire, the youngest of three girls. Although the Hollanders were always struggling to make ends meet they were a close-knit, loving family. The only thing that Sapphire resented, more than she ever dared admit, was wearing hand-me-downs, her older sisters' cast-offs. 'When I grow up I'm going to marry a rich man,' she vowed, one who could buy her all the new clothes she liked. It was a statement she was heard to utter often, especially when her eldest sister married a man without any prospects and lived in similar poverty. Sapphire could not understand why Jenny had chosen such a life for herself. Had she no ambition?

When Sapphire was sixteen she left school and got herself a job as an office junior with a large firm of printers; by the age of eighteen, after studying hard at evening classes, she became private secretary to the company buyer. Her next step, she vowed, was going to be personal assistant to the managing director.

She still gave most of her wages to her parents, because her father had recently been made redundant and times were harder than they had ever been. Sapphire still had no money for beautiful clothes, still made most of her own, but one day...

Drake Rivelin erupted into her life with the suddenness of a bolt of lightning—a tall, black-haired man, with an alive, interesting face, and a zest for life such as Sapphire had never seen before.

He was the owner of a company that manufactured fitted office furniture for the top end of the market. He believed in what he sold, and his enthusiasm came through every time he spoke.

Sapphire's company were considering placing an order, and after days of talks and decisions, when he shot in and out of her office without giving her a glance, she fell in love with him. Well, not exactly in love, but she admired everything that he stood for; ambition, his aura of power, a man who was stamping his mark in life, who knew what he wanted and was going all out to get it. It made her own efforts at success seem very mediocre.

One afternoon he stopped by her desk. 'I'm expecting an important phone call very shortly. Will you please put it straight through to Mr Brown's office?' His voice was deep-timbred and low-pitched, almost as though he were whispering words of love, and his light blue eyes rested on hers for much longer than was necessary.

Sapphire found herself unable to speak, simply nodding and gazing back into his eyes with a similar intentness. He really was a dangerously attractive man, not so much his looks but the power that he emanated—it was like an aphrodisiac, making her want to throw herself at him.

The next day a single yellow rose arrived on her desk. There was no name, no message, but when Drake Rivelin passed through to her boss's office with his usual whirlwind speed, he glanced at both it and her, and his smile was all-encompassing. She knew who the sender was.

Every day for a week another rose was delivered, and on Friday evening, when she worked late to type details of the order they were finally placing with Rivelin's company, he asked whether he could take her out to dinner. 'It's my fault you're having to work long past your normal time,' he said softly. 'It's the least I can do.'

His smile did things to her which should never have been allowed, and Sapphire wanted to say yes straight away, but caution made her hesitate. 'I hardly know you, Mr Rivelin,' she prevaricated. He had a wide, sensual mouth and white teeth that were not quite even.

Everything about him mesmerised her; she had never met a man before to whom she was instantly attracted, and she was unable to tear her gaze away.

'You've accepted my flowers,' he pointed out.

'Yes, and they're lovely, but——'

'Then you will come? Good. We'll go straight from here. Is there anyone you should ring to let know where you are?'

'My parents, but we're not on the phone,' answered Sapphire.

'Then I'll take you home and you can tell them. Perhaps you'll feel better if you change?'

Into what? she thought. None of her clothes had the elegance and glamour that she assumed were a part of his lifestyle. His own suit looked as though it had been made in Savile Row, cut to perfection so that it sat handsomely on his wide, powerful shoulders. Impeccably dressed and well groomed, a discreet, wafer-thin gold watch on his wrist, he was the epitome of the perfect male.

His car was an impressive BMW, and Sapphire felt uneasy in his presence. She had only ever dated boys her own age, boys in her own state of financial insecurity—not from her own choice, simply because no one else had ever asked her out. This man was at least ten years older and acted with an authority that was alien to her. It was like going out with her boss.

At home she felt uncomfortably aware of the shabbiness of the place, though Drake was charming to her parents and they treated him as if he were no different from anyone else. Only to Sapphire did he feel different! He was exciting, he was wealthy, he was overpowering!

She decided to wear a sage-green dress that complemented her shining auburn hair—her one redeeming feature. The dress wasn't new by a long chalk, but it was one of her better ones, home-made but not looking it, with a gently shaped skirt and fitted bodice, accentuating the soft curves of her breasts and the slenderness of her hips.

Drake Rivelin appraised her silently, but his lack of a compliment told Sapphire that he had expected her to look more glamorous. The image she had worked so hard to achieve of a confident young secretary sank into oblivion, and she wished she had never let him talk her into going out. She sensed that it was going to be a disastrous evening.

How wrong she was. Drake was friendly and amusing and attentive, and with every word and every glance he made her feel as though she were someone special. 'You're a unique, refreshing change from the girls I normally take out,' he told her. 'I'm enjoying this evening immensely.'

'Me too,' she whispered shyly.

'You're very beautiful.'

She said nothing.

'I've never met a girl with sapphire-coloured eyes. I presume you were named after them?'

'And because it's a precious stone,' she admitted. 'My parents chose it because they said I was precious to them.'

'Understandable,' he said with a faint nod and a smile. 'Have you any brothers or sisters?'

'Two sisters.'

'And do they have equally unusual names?'

Sapphire shook her head. 'Jennifer and Louise.'

'So why were you special?'

'Because I was their last child,' she confessed. 'My mother wanted a large family, but she couldn't have any more.' In fact, ever since she'd had Sapphire she had been plagued with ill health. Apparently the doctor had advised her, after a difficult birth with Louise, not to get pregnant again, but she had gone ahead anyway, and now, all these years later, she was still suffering the consequences.

When Drake took Sapphire home his kiss was disappointingly chaste, pricking the bubble of happiness that had been with her all evening, confirming her original opinion that she wasn't his type of girl. It was a thank-you for working late, that was all.

Again she was wrong. 'I've very much enjoyed this evening,' he said, an intent look in the light blue of his eyes. 'I have the whole weekend free in front of me, and it's unbelievably boring living in a hotel. Will you honour me with the pleasure of your company?'

Sapphire nodded and swallowed an aching lump in her throat. They were old-fashioned words, but Drake was not an old-fashioned man—far from it, being modern in dress and outlook, traditional only in his gentlemanly courtesy, something Sapphire had not found in any of the boys she dated. It was what made Drake different and romantic and so utterly attractive. She was in danger of being swept off her feet.

On Saturday they drove out to Stonehenge, viewing the world-famous site, deploring the fact that it was roped off and visitors could not go close up to the broken circle of impressive stones, the tallest of which was twenty-one and a half feet high. 'Have you ever been here on June the twenty-first?' asked Drake with a slight smile.

'The longest day of the year? Oh, yes, many times,' she answered. 'When the sun rises it casts the most dramatic shadows, makes the whole place feel mysterious. I can quite believe the theory that sun-worshipping ceremonies were held here nearly four thousand years ago.'

'I can think of better things to worship than the sun,' growled Drake, and when Sapphire looked at him his eyes were on her, an intense, hungry look in their depths that sent a shiver of sensuality through her body. He was saying that he found her attractive, that he wanted their relationship to develop into something deeper. And if the truth were known, so did she. He had captivated her from the very first moment she set eyes on him.

'Let's get away from here,' he muttered, taking her hand. 'There are far too many people about for my liking.'

They found a secluded spot by the River Avon, and to Sapphire's surprise he produced a picnic hamper filled with an astonishing selection of cold meats and cheeses, pâté de foie gras, turkey breasts, game pie, crusty bread, mango and kiwi fruits for dessert—and a bottle of Dom Perignon to accompany it all! Sapphire had never been treated so magnificently, and she looked at him in wonderment. He laughed. 'Only the best is good enough for a goddess.'

A goddess? He was calling her a goddess! She felt both embarrassed and flattered at the same time. They had known each other for such a short space of time; how could he feel this way?

'It's true, my sweet,' he said, seeing her confusion. 'I adore you—I've never met another girl who affects me like you do. The time we've known each other is immaterial; I know we're just right for each other.'

Sapphire laughed nervously. 'But you know nothing about me.'

'If it will make you happy,' he said with an indulgent smile, 'go ahead and tell me about yourself, but it really doesn't matter; it's you I'm interested in, not your background or your family, or past boyfriends, or what you've done with your life up till now.'

'I actually haven't done very much,' she confessed. 'The only holidays we've had have been in my uncle's caravan at Weston-super-Mare. I've never been abroad. I got a job when I was sixteen, I didn't stay on to get my A-levels, or go to college or anything like that, because we needed the money. I took a secretarial course at night school, and I've had a couple of boyfriends, but nothing serious. So you see, I've actually led a very boring life.'

'I don't agree,' he said. 'People's lives are different, but not boring. You seem to have been happy enough, and quite contented. Have you any ambitions?'

She nodded. 'To be PA to the managing director.'

'And that's the sum of it?' he asked with a faint frown.

'I always thought it was a pretty good ambition,' she returned defensively. 'It's well paid, and that's what it's all about these days.'

'Is money important to you?'

Sapphire hesitated before saying, 'Only in that I've never had any.' She did not want Drake thinking that she was interested in him because he was rich. It was a plus point, she had to admit it, but it wasn't the sole reason she was going out with him. He was a very attractive man in his own right. 'It would be nice to be able to go out and buy myself some nice clothes instead of making them, get a car, go on holidays abroad, that sort of thing.'

'Is marriage and children on your list?'

Sapphire shrugged. 'One day, yes, I suppose. I've never really thought about it; certainly not for a few years. I'm only twenty, and I want to enjoy myself first. Why haven't you ever tied the knot?' She imagined him to be somewhere in his thirties and most men his age were married. Perhaps he was a widower, or divorced? Or perhaps he *was* married and he hadn't told her! The thought caused her a moment's unease.

'I've been far too busy to get married,' he told her with a laugh. 'Why don't you help yourself to some food?'

Sapphire obediently filled her plate and bit into a piece of succulent turkey. It was delicious, and she was silent a moment as she ate, then, because she wanted to know more about him, she said, 'It's your turn now. Tell me about yourself.'

Drake finished his mouthful of game pie. 'What do you want to know?'

'Well, for starters, have you any brothers or sisters?'

'Not that I know of.'

Sapphire frowned and looked at him sharply. 'How can you not know?'

'The couple who brought me up, Rosemarie and Eric Willows, the couple I call mother and father, are not my real parents.' There was a sudden bitter edge to his voice, and Sapphire wondered whether she ought to call a halt to the conversation. She hadn't realised she could be digging up painful memories.

But before she could speak he went on, 'My father died when I was three years old, my mother remarried, but it didn't work out. She was very young and very beautiful, only sixteen when she had me; all she was interested in was a good time.' A muscle jerked in his jaw and his eyes became distant and hard. 'They split up, and Eric kept me because my mother's new boy-friend didn't want any snivelling kids, as he called them, getting in the way of their relationship.' Drake's lips were grim as he made the admission. It obviously hurt him very much that his mother had foresaken him so easily.

'That's awful. How could anyone do such a thing?' she asked, her voice full of compassion.

'That's a question I can't answer,' he grated. 'Eric Willows was a man in a million, however, and when he met and married Rosemarie they brought me up as their own. I shall be forever in their debt.'

She touched her hand to his arm, her navy eyes sympathetic. 'I can't believe that a mother would reject and forget her own child. Have you seen her since?'

Drake shook his head. 'Nor do I want to. Rosemarie and Eric mean more to me than she ever has, even though they've never officially adopted me. But enough of this—today is supposed to be a happy occasion.' He opened the bottle of champagne and filled two silver flutes. 'To us, my beautiful Sapphire, to a long and successful relationship.'

It was the first time Sapphire had ever drunk champagne, and the bubbles tickled her nose and made her laugh. 'This is unbelievable. Do you always do things in such a big way?' she asked.

'Only when I want to impress someone.'

'You're certainly impressing me,' she giggled, taking another drink of the sparkling liquid and holding her flute out for some more.

By the time the meal was over they had finished the bottle, and Sapphire felt as though she were floating on air. Drake packed the empty plates back into the wicker hamper and suggested a walk along the riverbank.

Hand in hand they went, laughing and talking, Sapphire feeling completely at ease with him, as though she had known him a lifetime instead of this being their second date. She marvelled at the instant rapport that had built up between them. She had always scoffed at the idea of love at first sight, but now it seemed a very definite possibility.

When Drake stopped walking, when he turned her into his arms and very gently kissed her, she soared with the eagles. No other kiss had ever had such an impact; her whole body felt as though it were on fire, sensation after sensation washing through her limbs in never-ending waves, and although the kiss started off experimentally, a gentle touching of their lips, it exploded now into raw animal hunger that took them both by surprise.

By the time they drew apart they were both gasping for air and Sapphire needed Drake's strong arms to support her. 'This wasn't what I intended,' he said gruffly. 'I apologise if I got carried away.'

'There's no need,' she husked. 'I—I felt the same. I don't know what came over me. I think it must be the champagne.'

'The champagne? Are you saying my sex appeal is in question?' he asked in mock dismay.

'Maybe you had a little bit to do with it,' she agreed with an impish smile.

'I hope it was more than a little bit,' he replied severely. 'Perhaps another kiss is in order, just to make sure?'

They made very sure.

On Sunday they spent the whole day together again, and Drake told her about his house in Cornwall which he had bought as a derelict farmhouse and fixed up until it was now a home he was proud of. 'I'll take you to see it one day,' he promised. 'I don't spend nearly enough time there, but fortunately I don't mind living in hotels.'

'So why do you keep it?' asked Sapphire. It seemed a waste of money to her.

'It's my bolt-hole, a place to go when I need peace and a rest from the hectic life I've created for myself. It's a real haven—you'll love it, I'm sure.'

She knew that Rivelin Office Furniture was based in Okehampton in Devon, and she learned now that it was about fifteen miles from Drake's home just over the border in Cornwall. 'I could move, I suppose,' he said, 'find somewhere more central, since a lot of my business is in the Home Counties, but I love the place too much to give it up, and there are good roads, so it's no real problem.'

Was he planning on raising a family there? Sapphire wondered, and although he had not hesitated to ask her whether she wanted babies she shied away from posing such a personal question. In any case, he seemed far too busy managing his business to find time to get married and bring up children.

In the days and weeks that followed Drake took her out frequently; he began buying her gifts of jewellery and clothes, seeming to know instinctively what size she wore, always choosing something that made her look and feel like a million dollars. He knew what suited her better than she did herself, and he was slowly transforming her from an ordinary girl no man would look at twice into a beautiful, elegant creature.

Sapphire found it hard to believe that it was happening, that she had actually met the man of her dreams, a man who could afford to shower her with presents and give her a taste of a lifestyle she had hitherto only imagined—and what was more astonishing was the fact that she was falling in love with him, that it wasn't only his money that interested her but Drake as a person. She really had the best of both worlds.

At first she fought to refuse his gifts, feeling embarrassed, feeling that he might really think it was his affluent lifestyle that attracted her, but his insistence wore her down, that and his smile and his kisses, which robbed her of all sane reasoning, and his undoubted approval of her in the fine new outfits. She felt like a different person, blossoming in his presence like a flower after much-needed rain.

Two months into their relationship he asked her whether she would give some serious thought to marrying him. Sapphire could not believe he had come to such a decision so soon; she had had her own fantasies, her own hopes and dreams, but she had never thought they would come true, she had never dreamt that a man like Drake could be seriously interested in someone like her. Her navy eyes grew wide, her heart throbbing so violently that it actually hurt.

Drake smiled tenderly, his eyes narrowing and softening as he looked at her in a way that was unique to him, in a way that made her feel she was more precious to him than anyone else in the whole world. 'My love, you look shocked,' he observed.

'I am,' she responded huskily. 'It's so soon—I never expected anything like this. I didn't realise you were serious.'

'It's what I've wanted ever since the first day I walked into your office,' he told her. 'You've no idea the impact you made on me. A beautiful English rose waiting to blossom, with an innocence about you that's most refreshing. But——' he looked serious all of a sudden '—there's something you need to know before you give me your answer.'

Whatever it was she would say yes, thought Sapphire. She loved him so very much, would marry him whatever the circumstances. Nothing could be so important that it would change her mind about him.

Warm, gentle hands, surprisingly gentle for so big a man—this gentleness in him had always surprised her—stroked her hair, moulded the shape of her head, framed her face, his eyes looked intently into hers, and several long seconds went by before he said, in a tone gruff with emotion, 'It's the question of children, my darling. This might come as a shock to you, but I—I'm afraid I don't want any. Not ever.'

CHAPTER TWO

A TINY cold hand clutched at Sapphire's heart. No children! A barren marriage! Could she live with that? Before she could speak Drake went on, 'No one truly knows whether a marriage will work out, and if it breaks down then it's always the children who suffer. I refuse to take that risk.'

He was speaking from personal experience, of course, and Sapphire could not blame him for thinking like that, but—no children, ever? Could she go through her life without them? As she'd once said to him, she had never given it any serious thought, but she'd always envisaged a family at some stage in her life. Was he being fair to her?

'I realise it's something you need to think about,' he said quietly. 'We should have discussed it before I mentioned marriage. I'm sorry, Sapphire, I——'

Sapphire stopped him; she had made up her mind. She loved Drake so much that she somehow did not care whether they had a family or not. He was all she wanted—and who knew? He might change his mind one day, especially when he found out that their marriage *was* going to last. She had no doubts about that, none at all. 'Drake, I'll marry you, whether we have children or not,' she told him. 'I love you, and all I want is to be with you forever.'

'You're sure about this?' he asked hoarsely. 'You wouldn't like more time to think about it? It's a very big step to take.'

'I'm positive,' she said with a wide smile.

'You'll have no regrets later, there'll be no come-backs, no trying to persuade me to change my mind?'

Sapphire shook her head. 'No, I promise you. You mean more to me than anyone in the whole world. Like you, the day I saw you I knew you were my other half, my destiny. I'll be content with you, Drake, for the rest of my life.'

The worried angles of his face relaxed into a warm, all-encompassing smile. 'My sweet, sweet Sapphire, you've no idea how happy you've made me.'

The wedding was fixed with incredible speed. Not that Sapphire minded—she loved this man with every fibre of her being, and although he had not actually said in so many words that he loved her, he had shown it in everything he did, in the gifts and the thoughtfulness and the gentle sharing and caring. She was indeed truly lucky that she had met such a man, and doubly lucky that he could give her the lifestyle she had always coveted. Could any girl be happier?

Her friends and sisters envied her, her parents were justifiably proud. Initially, when she had first told them Drake had asked her to marry him, they were worried about the expense, but Drake had a word with them, and although he did not tell Sapphire what had been said she guessed he was footing the bill, and doing it in such a way that he did not upset Jim or Betty. He really was a remarkable man.

He opened an account and put money into it, telling her to buy herself a fairy-tale wedding dress and a trousseau fit for a queen. 'I know how you girls set such store by these things, and I want you to look beautiful, my darling.'

Rosemarie and Eric Willows arrived from London the day before the wedding. They were booked into the same hotel that Drake was staying in, and Sapphire was duly introduced when they all met for a formal evening meal. Her initial anxiety was soon dispelled. They were wonderful people who welcomed her warmly into their family.

Marie, as she preferred to be called, was a tall, statuesque woman with steely grey hair and an outward appearance of reserve, yet with a warmth that soon became apparent. Eric was tall also, a serious, passionate man whose greatest love appeared to be books.

'I despaired of Drake ever settling down and getting married,' said his stepfather towards the end of the evening.

'I knew he was waiting for the right girl,' smiled the woman who had devoted herself to being a mother to him. 'You're going to be perfect, my dear. I've never seen two young people so much in love. I'm so happy for you both.'

The wedding ceremony itself passed as if in a dream, their honeymoon was a short, magical two weeks in the Bahamas, and then Drake took Sapphire back to his country house in Cornwall. Although he had promised to show it to her before they had somehow never found the time. Now she was entranced. The drive to it ran down between neatly shaven lawns with copper beech trees affording both shade and privacy. Treetops itself, a great rambling house, was painted white with a red-tiled roof and a white front door.

Even before she stepped inside Sapphire was in love with it, and once indoors she skipped from room to room, feeling like a child let loose in a shop full of toys. At the front of the house was Drake's study, a dining-room and library, and at the back the living-room and a huge kitchen, both of which overlooked the well-maintained gardens and the valley beyond with its rolling fields and dotted farmsteads. In the distance the hills were hazy and faintly purple.

'It's out of this world,' she said, twirling round to look at Drake, who was following her on her whirlwind tour.

'I'm glad you like it,' he told her with a pleased smile.

She ran upstairs to the bedrooms, and again was impressed. There were four bedrooms, each with its own bathroom, and the master room also had a dressing-room. She looked at the long line of wardrobes. 'I'll never have enough clothes to fill these,' she exclaimed.

Drake's mouth twisted wryly. 'From what I know about women they never have enough wardrobe space.'

A tiny stab of unexpected jealousy caused Sapphire a moment's pain. For the first time she wondered how many other girls there had been in his life. He had never mentioned any, but there must have been plenty; he had the sort of charm that drew women to him like moths to a flame. Which made it all the more amazing that he had chosen her. She truly hoped she would never let him down.

Prior to his marriage Drake had had a woman come in to do his cleaning; now, on Sapphire's insistence, she did it all herself, taking great pride and pleasure in keeping the house spotless. It was all so different from what she was used to, the sort of place she had always dreamed about, with exquisite pieces of period furniture, Aubusson carpets, paintings by the masters, Sèvres and Minton vases, Meissen figurines, in fact a veritable storehouse of all things beautiful.

Each evening she dressed up for Drake, and the pleasure in his eyes when he looked at her made her the happiest woman in the world. The physical side of their relationship was all and more than she had ever dreamed. Drake was a considerate, innovative, expert lover who excited her beyond measure, who took her to the heights and left her floating on air for days on end.

She naturally wanted to get another job, as looking after the house did not fill all her days, but Drake would not hear of it. 'There's no need, my sweet, just relax and keep yourself beautiful for me. I've arranged to transfer money into your account each month, and if it's not enough all you have to do is ask for more.'

Sapphire was overwhelmed by his generosity. In her wildest dreams she had never imagined a life like this. It was perfect—she had everything she had ever wished for, and more. Drake still stayed away overnight on occasions, though not as much as he had before their marriage. They both hated being apart and spent long periods on the telephone declaring how much they missed each other. On his return their lovemaking always took on whole new dimensions, almost making his absence worthwhile.

The first time he took her to his office Sapphire was extremely impressed. She knew Rivelin Office Furniture was not a small company, but she had not expected this imposing, purpose-built complex which housed a sophisticated suite of offices at the front, and warehouse and workshops at the back.

Drake took great pride in showing her round. 'All the furniture is made and assembled right here,' he told her as they walked through the workshops, 'and goes through rigid checks and inspections before it's ready to leave the premises.'

'You have a good reputation,' she remarked.

'And I personally make sure it's maintained. I pay high wages, but I insist on the best workmanship.'

Drake had a kindly word to say to all his men, and it was clear they revered him. When he introduced Sapphire she felt a warm welcome too; the atmosphere was one of a big happy family rather than employer and employees, and she guessed that this way he got the best out of them. She imagined also that Drake was not averse to rolling up his sleeves and helping out himself if necessary. He was a skilled carpenter, and told her that ten years ago he had started off as a one-man business. Her admiration for him grew in leaps and bounds.

Back in the office suite she was introduced to his PA, Hélène Graham, a blue-eyed, attractive blonde; his design manager, another glamorous woman, a brunette this time; his installations controller, Bryan Jones; his accounts office manager, yet another female, and his sales manager, female as well. All in all there were more women than men on the staff, all of them with ravishing good looks.

Sapphire did not say anything, but she felt faintly uneasy with all these beautiful women in her husband's life. Had he chosen the opposite sex deliberately, or had he gone strictly on qualifications? She would never know, but the jealousy that streaked through her was very real.

It happened so gradually that she did not realise at first that Drake was staying away more and more often. Although they spent their weekends together it got to the stage that she rarely saw him during the week, and she felt he was putting his business before her.

'It won't be for long, my darling,' he promised, when she tackled him. 'Just while the business is still growing. It needs me at the helm—I need to go out and see the customers, make sure everything is all right, no detail overlooked.' But it went on for month after month, until Sapphire sometimes felt like screaming at the unfairness of it all.

'Can't I come and work in your offices? Can't I do something to help?' she asked, but his answer was always the same.

'I don't need any help, sweetheart; I want you to stay at home and keep yourself beautiful for me. There must be thousands of girls who'd give anything to be in your place.'

And lots of beautiful girls working for him! she thought bitterly. The jealousy she had felt on the day he took her to his office had never faded, and when he stayed away overnight she often wondered whether one of these girls was entertaining him. It seemed odd that so many of his staff were female. There had to be a reason—and she could think of none other than that he was a virile man who needed the companionship of a pretty woman at all times.

Occasionally his parents came down to stay for a few days and the monotony was broken. Sapphire got on extremely well with Drake's mother; an instant affinity had sprung up between the two women, and they talked for hours on end about all manner of things. Marie did not approve of her son neglecting his new bride, and frequently told him so, but it made no difference. 'I'm securing our future,' he always said. 'Sapphire understands.'

For her twenty-first birthday, as well as throwing a lavish party, Drake bought her an expensive camera, and from that moment on Sapphire had an absorbing new hobby. To begin with, she snapped anything and everything, joining a photographic society, learning not only how to take good pictures but to develop her films too.

Flora became her favourite subject, and she discovered a natural talent. Her focusing and exposure were always spot-on, and she knew instinctively from which angle flowers or fungi looked their best. She was often out early in the morning when the sun was rising and everything was dew-spangled, or late in the day when the light was warm. She was always looking for a different angle, a different aspect, something that would make her pictures unique.

One of the professional members of the photographic society, Colin Radderton, had a darkroom at his studio in nearby Launceston, which he said Sapphire could use from time to time, and she spent many happy hours there developing her films and enlarging her photographs. She even managed to sell a few of her pictures to a gardening magazine, and was busy building up a portfolio to try and register herself with one of the photographic libraries. She felt quite excited by the new career she was building for herself, and the time passed much more quickly.

Oddly enough, it was the camera Drake had bought her to help while away the hours during his absence that caused their first major row. She had taken some photographs of a rare species of wild flower she had found growing on the cliffs at the Lizard, and was so anxious to get them developed that she worked until late in the evening. When her car would not start Colin, who lived in a flat above the studio, offered her a lift home.

She was surprised and pleased to see Drake's car on the drive, and after saying a quick thank-you and goodbye to Colin she ran eagerly the few yards to the front door, but her ready smile faded when a scowling Drake confronted her in the hall.

'Who the hell was that?' he barked, 'and where do you think you've been until this hour?'

Sapphire glanced at the Edwardian longcase clock. 'It's only ten,' she pointed out, and as if to emphasise her point it began striking the hour in its deep somnolent tones. 'I wasn't expecting you home, darling. You should have let me know, I'd have made sure I was back. I've been developing some films.'

'It's quite obvious you weren't expecting me,' he snarled savagely. 'How many other nights have you spent out with that bastard in the Citroën?'

Sapphire sent him a shocked glance. 'Drake, what are you saying? There's nothing between Colin and me—he's a happily married man old enough to be my father.'

'And I thought you were a happily married woman,' he growled. 'It seems I was mistaken. Here I am working my guts out to provide us with a decent living, and this is how you repay me. What have you to say about that?'

Sapphire shook her head in hurt bewilderment at her husband's harsh words. 'It's not like that, Drake. Colin often lets me use his darkroom, but this is the first time I've ever worked during the evening. When my car wouldn't start he ran me home—it's as simple as that.'

'He was working with you, was he?' sneered Drake. 'A cosy little twosome. Don't worry about Sapphire's husband, because he's never at home. I wonder how long this has been going on?'

'Your comments are uncalled for!' she shot back, her own temper beginning to rise now. 'You're making accusations that are entirely without foundation. I only took up photography because you're never here.'

'I'd never have bought the damn camera if I'd known it would take over your life,' he growled, taking her chin in a crippling grip and tilting her head back, his light blue eyes burning into hers. 'And now you're saying everything's my fault? You're saying that I neglect you?'

Sapphire jerked away. 'I've never said anything of the sort,' she protested, trying to quell the fierce pain in her chest. The anguish of loving this man who thought more of his job than he did of her was breaking her heart. 'But since you've brought up the subject, then yes, I do think you spend too much time at work. It's hardly fair on me, is it? And it's not right that you should complain when I try to keep myself occupied. You should be pleased that I have something to do.'

'Not pleased if it takes you into another man's arms.' His mouth was tight, his whole face a shuttered mask, and it was obvious he had formed his own opinion and nothing she could say would change it.

'This conversation's getting us nowhere,' cried Sapphire, shaking her head. 'I'm going to make myself some supper—do you want any?'

Drake's eyes were glacier-hard, almost slicing through her in their intensity. 'Food is the last thing on my mind at this moment. I had a table booked at Mulberry's, but, needless to say, when I found my wife absent I had to cancel. I find it amazing that your dear friend Colin didn't take you somewhere to eat.'

Sapphire felt like clawing her nails down his face. What on earth had got into him? It was the first time ever he had been this angry. Why wouldn't he believe her? Why did he persist in thinking that there was something going on between her and Colin? 'You could have told me on the phone last night that you were coming,' she protested, trying her hardest to keep her voice reasonable. Though when she came to think about it, he had sounded a bit strange, cutting the call much shorter than usual.

'I could have told you this afternoon, or yesterday afternoon, or the day before, if you'd been in when I telephoned,' he returned harshly. 'It strikes me that you're never at home these days.'

'Oh, Drake,' she said pleadingly, 'let's not argue like this. I'm sorry I was out tonight. I won't let it happen again.'

His face relented fractionally. 'And this guy means nothing to you?'

She shook her head. 'Not a thing; he's just letting me use his facilities.'

'You could have your own darkroom here, if your hobby's that important to you,' he growled. 'Hell, Sapphire, I don't want to argue either, but I've sat here for hours wondering where you were, and when you turned up with some other man I wanted to beat his brains out.'

He held out his arms and she went into them, his mouth sought and found hers and they kissed. 'I can't bear the thought of you going off with another man,' he growled, his hands sliding down to her buttocks, pressing her close to him so that their bodies fitted together like two halves of a whole.

This is how it should always be, thought Sapphire. I never want Drake to go away, I want him here with me; I don't want any empty nights alone, I want Drake in my bed, in my body, together with me at all times. Her desire for him flared without provocation, her groin ached with the intensity of her need, her breasts throbbed and hardened and her cheeks flamed with love and hunger.

Sensing the need in her, Drake lifted her up into his arms and carried her effortlessly and silently to their bedroom, setting her down gently on the edge of the bed, where his mouth once again claimed hers. It was obvious that he was as hungry for her as she was for him, his anger forgotten, his kisses growing in intensity and passion.

'My gorgeous, gorgeous girl, how could I possibly doubt you?' Adoration shone from his eyes and he teased her with feathery kisses on her forehead, her eyelids, her nose, her cheeks, finally crushing her lips, devouring her almost; and Sapphire's whole body trembled beside him.

Her head was thrown back, exposing the vulnerable arch of her throat, and he nuzzled his face against it, slipping her blouse from her shoulders, snapping open the front fastening of her bra, tenderly, lovingly stroking her breasts.

Sapphire's nipples grew taut and hard beneath his caress and she fell back on the duvet, closing her eyes, revelling in the feel and touch of this man whom she loved more than life itself. Her skirt was eased from her hips, her delicate lace panties following, and his hand slid over her flat stomach to the trembling heart of her.

A tiny moan of sheer ecstasy came from Sapphire's lips and she arched herself upwards, needing him, wanting him desperately. She sensed a similar urgency in Drake, but as always he took his time, pleasuring her first, knowing exactly where to touch her to create sensations so infinite, so intense, so beautiful that she felt close to tears.

She was not aware of the exact moment that he took off his own clothes, she knew only that when he lay next to her bare skin met bare skin, hers warm and scented and soft, his firmer and hair-roughened and very, very masculine.

He kissed her breasts, first one and then the other, sucking her nipples into his mouth, biting gently, hurting and yet pleasuring at the same time. He trailed a burning pathway of kisses over her stomach to her thighs and her legs parted willingly. His mouth and tongue ravished her senses, sending her delirious with desire, and she ached for him to possess her completely.

When he finally entered her she wrapped her legs around him, matching his rhythm as she had from the very first time they had made love on their honeymoon in the Bahamas. She had marvelled then that they seemed so finely attuned, and she marvelled again now. Always it was like this, always Drake took her to the very limit of physical pleasure, making her feel she was going to burst with the intensity of it all. Nothing she had ever heard about making love had prepared her for this excitement beyond all measure.

They reached the pinnacle together, crying out aloud as their passion peaked, shuddering and clinging, feeling wave after wave of the sweetest pain man could ever experience undulating through them, racking their limbs, until finally they lay spent in each other's arms.

It seemed to Sapphire that they spent the whole night making love, and Drake promised her faithfully that he would try not to be away from home so much. 'It's not that I don't miss you, darling—I do,' he muttered thickly. 'It tears me in two having to be away from you, but the trouble is the business needs me. It's our future I'm securing. Give me time, my sweetest angel; one day it will be a nine-to-five job. I swear to you.'

For a while he kept his word. He was away no more than a couple of nights a week; but then he said he was thinking of expanding into the Midlands. Up until now he had only covered southern England. 'I'm afraid it means I'll be away quite a lot to begin with,' he told her ruefully. 'It could mean occasional weekends as well.'

Sapphire looked at him in open-mouthed astonishment. 'I can't believe you're going to do this to me, Drake. Am I expected to sit back and put up with even longer absences without saying a word?' She hadn't been feeling well lately, somehow drained of all energy, ever since their first argument, in fact, and she put it down to depression. Drake spending even more time away from home was the last thing she wanted. 'Can't I come with you? I could help, I'm sure; I am a qualified secretary, after all. I could take notes—I could do almost anything.'

But Drake shook his head. 'Darling, you wouldn't stand the pace. It's a hectic life, one of my own making, I know, but I love the cut-and-thrust of business. The company really is making a name for itself, and expanding further north is a natural progression.'

'Can't anyone else take over the new area?' she asked. 'Do you have to do it yourself?'

He took her into his arms. 'Darling, please understand how much this means to me. It's not as if you have nothing to do, and I'm still prepared to furnish you with a darkroom if that's what you want.'

'No, thank you.' Her tone was prim. 'It would be a waste of money when I can use Colin's.'

It was the first time the other man's name had been mentioned since the day he had brought her home, and Drake's lips tightened ominously. 'I didn't realise you were still seeing him.'

'I'm not *seeing* him,' she protested sharply. 'I use his darkroom, that's all.' Though not so much as she had in the past, because Colin needed it more and more himself. It would actually be ideal to have a darkroom of her own, but a stubborn streak made her turn down Drake's offer. He seemed to think that spending money on her solved all their problems.

'And I don't see why I shouldn't go on using it,' she continued. 'I have nothing to hide whatsoever. I feel insulted and hurt that you think I'd be unfaithful. It's not my own choice that I'm left on my own such a lot. For all I know you could be the one who's having an affair. Who knows what you get up to all those nights you spend away from home?'

A flare of anger lit up the light blue of his eyes. 'Is that really what you think?' he asked harshly, pushing her from him and stepping back a pace.'

'How do I know what you do?' Her beautiful eyes flashed her resentment. 'I've suggested coming with you, but you turned that idea down flat. There must be a reason. Maybe there are other women in your life.'

'This whole conversation is getting ridiculous,' he snarled. 'There's no one else but you, Sapphire—you should know that. All I do when I'm away is work. You know how much my business means to me.'

'And I know that you always put it first. It's clearly the most important thing in your life, more important than me. You'll never let go the reins. After the Midlands it will be the north of England and then Scotland, until you're a truly national company, and you'll still want to run it all by yourself. I don't think I can take much more of it, Drake. It's obvious you're not cut out to be a married man, and I'm not cut out to be a sit-at-home wife. I want you here with me.'

'Oh, my darling, it's what I want too.' He took her into his arms and held her close, and their two hearts throbbed, but no longer in unison, thought Sapphire. The business excited him more than she did. 'But this really is an enormous challenge, sweetheart. I'm even thinking about moving into bigger premises to cope with it all. Everything's happening, and I have to be right at the centre of it; I don't want to miss out on any of the action. Please be patient, just for a little while longer.'

When he looked at her with that boyish, pleading expression in his eyes she could not remain angry with him. 'I miss you so much,' she said huskily.

'And I miss you, darling, more than words can say. I'll try my very hardest to be home as much as I can.'

But once the wheels were set in motion his periods away grew longer and longer. He never failed to telephone, and yellow roses arrived almost daily until she was sick and fed up with them. When he came home he brought jewellery and perfume and any other trinkets that he thought she might like, but as far as Sapphire was concerned they were nothing more than conscience-appeasers. She was no longer excited by gifts from him.

She was fast discovering that having plenty of money didn't necessarily make you any happier, and she found it more and more difficult to be civil.

They argued frequently, and more than once Drake threw Colin's name in for good measure, seeming to think she was still carrying on some sort of an affair. After one particularly volatile weekend, when they had done nothing but sling accusations at each other, Sapphire could stand it no longer. 'Don't be surprised if I'm not here when you come back next time,' she slammed at him furiously. 'I've had about as much of this as I can take.' The trouble was he was her whole life, whereas she was only a small part of his. He did not need her as she needed him.

Drake's eyes narrowed disbelievingly and his voice was as cold as ice. 'You seem to forget I'm doing this for us, Sapphire, so that we'll have a comfortable and secure future. If you can't put up with a few nights on your own then you're not the girl I thought you were.'

'A few nights?' she shrieked. 'A few months, if you add it all up.'

'So what's a few months out of a lifetime?' he asked. 'I get home as often as I can, Sapphire, I really do. If you can't accept that then perhaps I will be better off without you.'

Sapphire could not believe they were saying these things. Her threat to leave had not been serious, she loved him far too much; and she had certainly never expected this kind of reaction. She had thought he would implore her not to do anything so silly, tell her he loved her and couldn't live without her; instead he was implying that if she wanted to leave then he wouldn't stop her.

That night Drake slept in one of the other bedrooms and Sapphire cried herself to sleep. Perhaps he didn't love her any more? Perhaps there was already another woman in his life? Sapphire did not know what to think; all she knew was that the bed had never felt so empty, and she wanted to go to him and beg him to make love to her. Always, after every single one of their arguments, they had made it up in bed. She hated to think that things were so bad he did not want to sleep with her.

But pride forbade her to go to him, and the next morning it was too late. When she awoke he had already left the house. It was the first time he had ever done that without kissing her goodbye, and Sapphire felt as though her whole world had come to an end. Nor did he telephone her that evening, and when she rang his hotel—he always told her where he was staying—she discovered that his reservation had been cancelled.

So where was he? She began to get worried, and at nine the next morning, as soon as his office opened, she telephoned his personal assistant. 'Mrs Rivelin!' exclaimed Hélène Graham in surprise. 'Drake said you were going away on holiday. Is something wrong?'

Sapphire gasped. 'Yes, very wrong,' she snapped, and slammed down the receiver. Drake had gone away! Without her! It was unbelievable. And if his PA assumed they were together it must mean that he had taken another woman with him. What other explanation could there be? She felt numb with shock and groped for a seat before her legs gave way beneath her.

How often had this happened before? How often had she thought Drake was working himself to a shadow when all the time he was enjoying himself with another female? It could have happened no end of times, because never had she telephoned him, always he had rung her. A holiday, indeed! They'd had no more than a few days away in the whole of the two years they'd been married; Drake never had the time, he said, so how was it he could manage it for someone else?

The blood drained out of her and she felt physically ill. He had had the gall to accuse her of having an affair with Colin when all the time he had been guilty of doing the same thing. She could not credit it, it did not make sense—or did it? Had she been too gullible? Ought she to have known that no man would stay away from home so long unless he was tiring of his wife?

All day she walked around the house in a state of shock, her thoughts whirling, her mind totally confused; and when her friend Caroline, whom she had met at the photographic society, came on one of her frequent visits, Sapphire told her the whole sorry story.

Caroline grimaced instead of looking stunned. 'I guess you had to find out some time,' she said.

'What do you mean?' Sapphire frowned and a nasty feeling tightened her stomach.

'Well,' said her friend, 'I would never have said anything if this hadn't happened, but I've actually seen Drake myself on more than one occasion with another woman.'

Sapphire felt as though all the wind had been knocked out of her sails. She thought for a minute that she was going to pass out, and clung to the arms of her chair until the sensation passed. 'You've seen him and you've never told me?' she said huskily.

Caroline shrugged in sympathy. 'I didn't want to hurt you.'

'So where did you see them, and what's she like, this woman?' demanded Sapphire.

Caroline heaved a sigh, as though wishing she had never said anything. 'Long blonde hair, slender; I've never actually seen her face, you understand, as she always had her back to me. In a hotel in London, actually, and——'

'In a hotel?' Sapphire cut in furiously. 'Booked in together?'

'I don't know,' said Caroline with a tiny shrug. 'I've only ever seen them in the restaurant. I'm often in London, as you know, and they seem to use the same place.'

'Didn't Drake ever notice you?' Sapphire asked sharply.

'No,' admitted her friend reluctantly. 'He's always been so deep in conversation that he's oblivious to everyone else in the——'

'Enough!' Sapphire shook her head in savage anger. 'It's quite obvious the swine's been two-timing me. Would you mind going, Caroline? I have a lot of thinking to do.' There was a whole world of difference between guessing that Drake might be two-timing her and being confronted with hard, cold facts.

The other girl touched Sapphire's arm in gentle compassion. 'I don't think you should be on your own,' she said. 'This has been a great shock to you, and you need some support.'

'I don't even think I should be *here*,' raged Sapphire in sudden decision. 'If he can go away without me, then I can certainly go away without him. He doesn't deserve a wife. My God, when I think what I've put up with over the last two years, and then he does this to me!' Her breath came out in sharp, angry jerks and she shook her head so violently that she felt dizzy. 'I have to get away for a while, Caroline. Let the swine suffer when he comes back and finds me missing. What I wouldn't give to know where he is; I'd be there like a shot and give him the biggest shock of his life.'

'He's such an attractive man,' said Caroline. 'I've always envied you. He's every woman's dream. He must have lots of girls making up to him, but I never thought he'd do this to you. Until I saw him for myself he always gave me the impression of being very loyal.'

'Well, now we both know what he's like,' stormed Sapphire.

Caroline nodded. 'If you really want somewhere to go, my sister has a holiday cottage in Lanreath. It's standing empty at the moment because she's been having a bathroom put in upstairs. I'm sure she'd let you stay there for a while.'

'It could be just what I need,' said Sapphire.

'If you want my opinion, I think you'll be doing the right thing,' went on Caroline. 'Drake needs teaching a lesson. Lorna's cottage will be a bit of a comedown, though, after living somewhere like this.' She looked around her enviously.

'Money isn't everything,' said Sapphire sharply. It was something she had found out the hard way. All those years she had dreamt of marrying a rich man, had been beside herself with joy when she had found one, with the added bonus of loving him as well, and now—what had she got? Nothing but an empty life. Drake was so intent on making the filthy stuff that he hadn't got time for her. Money, at this moment, was the least of her problems.

She was doing quite well with her photography. She had managed to get accepted by one of the picture libraries and a lot of her work was selling. In fact, she was making quite a name for herself, although she had never told Drake exactly how successful she was, because he didn't show much interest, believing it to be nothing more than an amusing hobby.

The cottage was perfect, built of stone, colourwashed pink, roses climbing all over it, with a private back garden but nothing at all at the front. Lorna Brecon, Caroline's sister, was willing to let Sapphire rent it for as long as she liked.

Lanreath was situated a few miles from the popular fishing harbours of Looe and Polperro on the south coast of Cornwall, a small, quiet village with an interesting Norman church, a folk and farm museum which also gave demonstrations of rural crafts, a sixteenth-century inn, a post office and general stores and a little tea-room where they also did bed and breakfast. Sapphire loved it. She turned one of the bedrooms of the cottage into the darkroom she coveted, and her whole life revolved around her photography.

She had made Caroline swear she would never tell Drake where she was. 'I'll go back in my own good time,' she said, and the way she felt at the moment it would be never.

Every week, during the two years she had been married, Sapphire had always phoned her parents—they had had a telephone installed shortly before her wedding, and she guessed Drake had something to do with it—and about once a month she and Drake went to see them. They understood that with Drake working so hard it was impossible for them to visit more frequently, but never had she told them there was anything wrong with her marriage, nor did she now.

She still telephoned and chatted and pretended there was nothing wrong, never giving any indication that she had left Drake. But when her father told her that her mother was going into hospital for a serious and long-overdue operation Sapphire immediately put her own problems behind her and went to see them.

The operation was performed successfully and her mother sent home soon afterwards because of a shortage of hospital beds. She still needed medical care, and Sapphire didn't think twice about using the allowance Drake made her to pay for a private nurse. She had been shocked to see how old her parents were looking these days, and it would be a long time before her mother completely recovered. Louise had married last year, and her father was absolutely no good when it came to looking after a sick person. Sapphire was worried to death about them both.

Initially, she had vowed not to touch a penny of her husband's money, but this was something different; this was a matter of life and death. She would pay it back afterwards out of her photography money. There was no way she wanted to be beholden to him.

Inevitably the truth came out that she had left Drake, and her parents' distress emphasised her own pain. 'I would never have believed that Drake would do such a thing,' said her mother. 'I would have gambled my life on him being a loyal and faithful husband.'

'That's what I thought,' said Sapphire quietly, not letting them see how hurt she really was. The fact that Drake hadn't once contacted her parents to find out if they knew where she was proved that he loved his business—*and his mistress*—more than he loved her.

She stayed until she was sure her mother was well on the road to recovery and then went back to Lanreath. She had told her parents where she was living, but made them promise not to divulge her address to Drake. 'I'll get in touch with him in my own good time,' she said. 'If he does contact you, though I doubt it after all these weeks, then tell him I'm in London or something.'

When she discovered that she was pregnant Sapphire was at first horrified and then happier than she had been since leaving Drake, and she couldn't think why she hadn't known earlier. She had thought the trauma in her life was responsible for the change in her body cycle, and as she had gained no weight there had been nothing else to tell her about her condition.

She knew exactly when it had happened—three months ago when he had accused her of having an affair with Colin, when they had made passionate love long into the night. It was not until the next morning that she remembered she had forgotten to take her pill. She had hoped one day wouldn't matter.

In all the two years they had been married Drake had not changed his mind about wanting a family, and she knew without a doubt that he wouldn't want this baby growing inside her now; but she did—she wanted it desperately; she hadn't realised until this moment what it would have meant to go all her life without children. How could she have ever thought she would be happy and satisfied?

She decided not to tell her parents about the baby yet because she knew the pressure they would put her under to go back to Drake. It was with great reluctance that they had agreed not to divulge her address, and she was sure that if they knew about the baby they would not hesitate to break that promise.

The fact that she was pregnant did not stop her from working, and working hard. She had been hailed as an exciting new talent and was receiving commissions from various magazines and all sorts of unlikely places, and she lugged around her camera bag, filled to bulging with lenses and camera bodies and filters and all the rest of her essential equipment, without a thought that she could do any harm to herself.

Whether it was that, or whether it would have happened in any case, she could not be sure, but at five months Sapphire suffered a miscarriage. She was totally distraught; she had wanted this baby so much, more than anything else in the whole wide world. Life suddenly had no meaning. She stopped taking photographs, she almost stopped eating. She shut herself indoors. She didn't cry, she was too distressed for that, and if it hadn't been for her next-door neighbour she would have let herself go altogether.

Robin Featherstone was a man in his late thirties, a widower with a daughter of seventeen away at college. He had been pensioned off from his job because of a back injury and spent most of his time carving animals out of bits of old wood. He was actually very good at it, and had sold quite a few. They had had some long and interesting conversations, but Sapphire had never encouraged him or invited him into her house.

Now, though, Robin became her constant companion, talking her out of her apathy, encouraging her to get out and about again, going for long walks with her, insisting, as she got stronger, that she begin taking photographs again. He was her mainstay, and Sapphire did not know what she would have done without him.

She realised now that there was no point in ever attempting a reconciliation with Drake. If the miscarriage had done nothing else it had taught her that she had made a grave mistake in marrying him. She definitely wanted children. She wanted a family around her, she wanted the pleasure of watching them grow up.

Eventually she was back to full health and vigour and didn't need Robin in her life, but the friendship lingered, and often he took supper with her or she with him. It was a comfortable relationship, with no sex involved at all, although Sapphire had the feeling that he would not need much encouragement.

She still visited her parents frequently, and she had finally told them about the baby, but they had given up asking about Drake, sensing that it was a subject she did not wish to discuss.

When she was asked to photograph the gardens of a National Trust property near Launceston she knew she would not be able to pass so close to Treetops without taking a quick look at it. But never had she dreamt that she would encounter her husband.

CHAPTER THREE

AS SHE drove back to her cottage home in Lanreath Sapphire's thoughts were in turmoil. She could not get over the fact that Drake thought she had married him for his money, and it hurt all the more because there was actually a shred of truth in it, though not very much. Her love for him had surpassed all other aspirations and ambitions. Her sin had been in the mind, nothing else, and he had no right to accuse her of such a thing. When she left she had taken only her clothes, her photographic equipment and the car he had bought her as a wedding present. She had opened a new account entirely for the money she earned from her photography and used only that, and if her mother hadn't been ill she would have touched none of his allowance.

The fact that she got home safely from Treetops was more by luck than judgement. She could remember nothing of the journey; her mind was in complete chaos. Instead of garaging the car she left it outside, stripped off her jacket, and threw herself down in despair on the chintz-covered sofa. The whole situation was totally unbelievable.

Almost immediately a tap came on the door. Sighing impatiently, Sapphire pushed herself up again. Robin Featherstone had a frown of concern on his face. 'Sapphire, I saw you come in. What's wrong? You look awful.'

'Everything's wrong,' she snapped harshly. 'I've just been speaking to my husband.'

'Oh, I'm sorry,' he said with a grimace. 'I didn't realise. You obviously need to be alone—I'll go.'

'No, no, come in. You can make a pot of tea.' Sapphire went back to her seat, and Robin busied himself in the kitchen. He was as much at home here as in his own house these days, and in less than five minutes he was back with two steaming cups which he set down on an occasional table drawn up to the sofa.

'You look as though you've had some kind of shock, so I've made it very sweet. That is the usual remedy, isn't it?' Robin had mousy brown hair that was fast receding and going grey, his face was round and pleasant, though not by any stretch of the imagination could he be called handsome. Nevertheless, Sapphire liked him a lot.

'I believe so, though I'm not sure it does any good.' She sat up and sipped the hot, sweet liquid, grimacing slightly as she normally took her tea without sugar, but somehow it had a soothing effect.

Robin sat and said nothing. He was wonderful in that respect. He always knew when to talk or when to sit quiet. He was a perfect companion; he never probed, never asked questions. If Sapphire wanted to tell him something that was all right, if she didn't then that was all right too.

'My husband's a bastard.'

The words shocked Robin. He had never heard his neighbour use that kind of language before.

'He's an out-and-out swine, and I hate him.'

He lifted an eyebrow, but still didn't speak.

'He thinks I'm after his money,' she went on.

'I thought you were doing very well at your photography? You've always struck me as being very independent and self-sufficient.'

'I am,' she said grimly. 'His accusation was entirely unfounded—that's what hurts so much.'

'Tell me to shut up if it's none of my business, but what made you go to see him?' She had already told Robin the reason she had left Drake.

'I didn't,' said Sapphire. 'Well, I didn't mean to. I was just looking at the house; it does, after all, hold a lot of memories, most of them happy. I thought Drake would be at work. I had the shock of my life when he pulled up behind me. But for him to think I was there intending to beg for money—what an insult. I wouldn't demean myself even if I were penniless.'

An hour or more went by before she calmed down, and even then she could not get Drake's accusation out of her mind.

'You need something to take your mind off it,' said Robin firmly. 'Why don't we have a day out tomorrow? We'll set off early, go to London, perhaps. We could even stay a few days.'

Sapphire looked at him with a spark of interest. 'There's an exhibition on at the Photographers' Gallery, we could go to that.' It was exactly what she needed to take her mind off Drake.

'Whatever you like, if it will make you happy. I hate seeing you like this.'

Sapphire wished Drake had wanted her happiness just as much. His whole purpose in life was making money; she came a poor second best. Briefly she touched Robin's cheek. 'You're quite a guy—a girl couldn't wish for a better friend. We'll go tomorrow.'

But before she had even got up the next morning there came a resounding knock on her door. Looking out of the bedroom window, she saw a white BMW—the same one that had pulled up behind her at Treetops!

Without even stopping to pull on a wrap Sapphire ran down the stairs and yanked open the door, just as Drake's hand was raised to pound it again. She glared at him stormily. 'What the hell are you doing here? Did you follow me yesterday?' The very thought sent an angry shiver down her spine.

For a moment he did not speak. His hooded eyes looked into hers, and then slowly and deliberately studied the whole length of her. Her cotton nightshirt with its *Love is*... motif was almost indecently short and her long, slender legs held his scrutiny for much longer than was necessary. It took an age for his eyes to come back to her face, pausing unhurriedly on the thrust of her breasts, as if he was remembering the times he had touched and kissed her, aroused her to such depths of passion that she had pleaded with him to make love to her again and again. Whatever else had gone wrong with their marriage it hadn't been the physical side of it.

'Aren't you going to ask me in, or do you make a habit of standing on the doorstep in your nightclothes?' he grated.

Sapphire's eyes flashed at the caustic edge to his tone, and reluctantly she stood back. The last thing she wanted was Drake inside her cottage—this was her retreat, her own private place where there were no memories of him.

He looked about the room with interest, at the deep, comfortable chairs, at the open fireplace where a vase of cut flowers made a bright splash of colour, at the paintings on the walls and the books on the shelves. 'Very cosy,' he admitted, 'though I thought you'd have spent my money on something more elegant. Are you happy here?'

'I was until you came,' she snapped, and deliberately ignoring his gibe about money, went on, 'What do you want?'

'Is that any way to greet your husband?' His narrowed eyes were watchful on hers.

'As far as I'm concerned you're no longer my husband,' she told him coldly, wondering whether she ought to get dressed properly, or at least put on a dressing-gown. But that would tell him he disturbed her, and the last thing she wanted was him guessing that he still had that power. 'Leaving you was the best thing I ever did.'

'You enjoy living by yourself?' He sat down in one of the armchairs, sinking back into it, crossing one leg over the other, looking as if he was prepared to stay for a long time.

Sapphire nodded, though it was a lie. Apart from her photography her life was empty. She missed Drake more than she liked to admit.

'And yet you didn't enjoy being in my house by yourself,' he rapped. 'What's the difference?'

She flashed him a look of contempt. 'Isn't it obvious? I don't spend hours now waiting for you to come home, wondering when I'm going to see you again. My days are clearly mapped out, I come and go as I please.'

'Don't you miss having a man in your bed?'

'How often did I have you?' she snapped. 'It's far better this way.'

His lips compressed. 'I didn't come here to pick an argument, Sapphire.' He stood up again and moved purposefully towards her.

'No?' she asked, backing away, her heart pitter-pattering. 'So why did you come?' She hoped it wasn't to ask her home.

'As I said yesterday, we need to talk.'

'About what?' she asked sharply.

'You and me.'

Her eyes flashed savagely as she glared at him. 'There's nothing to be said. It's over, Drake—over, finished, done with.'

'Just like that?'

'It wasn't a spur-of-the-moment decision,' she pointed out. 'It had been on the cards for a long time. The trouble was you were so busy with your damn work you couldn't see it coming. You either didn't know or didn't want to know what you were doing to me.' She deliberately refrained from pointing out that his affair had been the last straw. If he didn't want to bring the matter up, then nor would she. She still had her pride left if nothing else. Her morale had been whipped raw by the fact that he sought the company of another woman, but she was damned if she would admit it. Let him think it was all because of the long hours he worked. 'Nothing you can say now will change my mind,' she went on determinedly, 'so there's no reason for you to stay.' She walked towards the door, but Drake was in front of her.

'Aren't you even going to offer me a cup of coffee after I've come all this way?' he demanded.

Sapphire took a deep breath and looked at him coldly. 'Very well, one quick cup, and then you're going.'

'Something tells me you don't like me being here?' The hard glitter in his eyes revealed barely suppressed anger.

'How very perceptive of you,' she hissed through gritted teeth.

'Why?'

Several seconds went by before she gave him her answer, long heart-stopping seconds when their eyes met and held and she could not be sure whether it was love or hatred that caused the fluttering in her stomach. 'You belong to my past.'

'And I have no part in your future, is that what you're saying?'

Sapphire did not answer; she swung on her heel and marched into the kitchen. Heavens, she wanted him with every fibre of her being, but things had changed. She wouldn't be happy in a childless marriage any longer. Besides, there was his neglect of her, his infidelity. How could she know it wouldn't happen again? How did she know that he wasn't still continuing his affair?

She filled the kettle, and when she turned he was leaning against the door-jamb watching her. More than ever Sapphire wished she had pulled on a dressing-gown. She felt far too vulnerable. It reminded her of the early days in their marriage, only then Drake would not have been satisfied with standing watching, he would have come across the kitchen and slid his hands beneath her nightdress, taking possession of her body, stimulating and arousing as only he knew how.

Quickly she banished her thoughts and concentrated on the job in hand. If he did not speak she could pretend he was not there. But it wasn't that simple. The small kitchen was filled with his presence; the air became so thick that she found it difficult to breathe. He was not the type of man you could ignore, not in any circumstances.

When the spoon caught the edge of the mug and coffee granules spilled on to the worktop she hoped she had not given herself away—a vain hope, when the next second his hand touched her arm. 'Here, let me do it,' he ordered.

His touch sent fire coursing through her veins, started a whole gamut of emotions over which she had no control. What had happened to her pride? she asked herself angrily. Why was she still feeling like this? Why couldn't she hate him? She was debating whether to slip away and get properly dressed when she heard Robin's familiar tap on the door.

She had almost forgotten in the confusion of Drake's arrival that they had arranged to go to London and agreed on an early start. Without a glance at her husband she hurried to the door.

Robin seemed surprised that she wasn't dressed. 'I saw the car,' he said. 'Are we still going to London, or is there a change in our plans? If we——'

'We're most definitely going,' said Sapphire firmly. 'My—er—visitor isn't staying long.'

'Oh, but he is.' Drake's deeply resonant voice came over her shoulder. 'I'm in no hurry to go at all, my darling, so you'd better tell your—*friend* to shove off.' The last words were spat out with sudden venom.

Robin's light brows rose at the unexpectedness of this attack. He looked at Drake and then back at Sapphire. 'Your husband?'

She nodded.

'Do you want me to stay?' There was sudden concern in his voice, a need to protect her from this man who had messed up her life.

'No, she damn well does not,' growled Drake.

'Sapphire?' questioned the other man.

She lifted her shoulders with a defeated shrug. 'You'd better go, Robin.'

'You'll be all right?' His brow was furrowed in a frown of concern.

'Yes.'

'Well, you know where I am if you need me. All you have to do is shout.'

'Thank you,' she said softly.

Reluctantly her neighbour left. Drake slammed the door shut and rounded on Sapphire. 'Who the hell was that?' he demanded.

'My next-door neighbour and a very good friend,' she answered, her eyes sparking fire, her whole body on the defensive.

'And he's taking you to London? My God, I don't believe this! Is he your new lover? First Colin and then—Robin, did you call him? Have you gone on to older men, is that it?'

The fury in his tone sent an ice-cold shiver down Sapphire's spine. 'What I do is no longer any concern of yours,' she answered with as much dignity as she could muster.

'Oh, but it is—you're still my wife,' Drake assured her tersely.

Sapphire allowed her eyebrows to slide up in disdain. 'I'd never have guessed it, the way you treated me. I thought you were married to your work.'

There was sudden blazing anger in his eyes, and without another word he returned to the kitchen. Sapphire took the opportunity to run upstairs, to wash quickly and pull on a pair of jeans and a pink T-shirt, and after dragging a brush through her hair she rejoined him.

His glance was cold and critical. 'I preferred the nightshirt,' he said.

Sapphire glared and said nothing, simply picking up the mug of coffee he slid across the counter, cradling her hands around its comforting warmth. She felt chilled through to her bones, even though it was midsummer. 'I want you to get out,' she said coldly. 'This is my cottage, and you're not welcome.'

'Really?' There was a hint of humour in the light blue eyes. 'Now that's a pity, because I've taken quite a liking to the place. I think I might even stay for a few days.'

Sapphire drew in a sharp, disbelieving breath. 'Now that is a turn-up for the books,' she jeered. 'What's happened? Have you found someone else to look after your precious business?'

'It can manage without me for a while,' was all he said. 'How many bedrooms have you got? No, forget I asked that—we'll only need yours.'

Sapphire gasped her indignation. 'You swine! If you think you can resume where we left off you're very much mistaken. All that was finished the day I walked out. I want nothing more to do with you.' And she certainly did not want him moving in with her.

Fury darkened Drake's brow and a muscle jerked out of control in his jaw. 'Because of lover-boy next door?' he growled. 'Is that it? I'll tell you this now, Sapphire, he'd better not set foot inside this house while I'm here or there might be some very unpleasant consequences.'

'I think you've lost all rights to dictate what I should or should not do,' she responded haughtily, drawing herself up to her full height and glaring with equal anger into the fierce blue of his eyes. 'I am now my own person and I can invite whom I like into my own home.'

'A home presumably bought with *my* money?' he counteracted harshly.

'Damn you, Drake,' she cried. 'You haven't changed, have you? You still think money is the be-all and end-all, the most important thing in the world. Well, let me tell you, it's not. I can vouch for it. Money brought me no happiness,' even though she had thought it would, 'and this cottage happens to be rented.'

'Money didn't bring you happiness?' A cynical, triumphant smile curved the fullness of his lips. 'Now that's good to hear.' Sapphire frowned, but before she could ask what he meant he went on, 'Tenancies are very easy to terminate. It would be quite a simple matter to get you turned out of here.' And with a sudden change of tone, with whiplash hardness that made her flinch, 'I want you back, Sapphire, and you ought to know that whatever I want I usually get.'

Sapphire took a stunned step backwards, her heart missing a beat, then continuing with frantic haste. 'You have a nerve, Drake Rivelin. In six whole months you haven't once tried to find me, and now you're saying you want me back. You know what you can do, don't you? You can go to hell. Two years was a fair enough trial as far as I'm concerned—more than enough, in fact. I have no intention whatsoever of living with you again. Whatever feelings I had for you are dead.'

Lies, all lies, she still loved him with all her heart, but resuming their marriage would solve nothing. She ought to have realised right from the beginning what sort of a lifestyle she was committing herself to. She had known that Drake rarely went home, that he always lived in hotels, but she had been so besotted that she had seen no further than her own immediate happiness. She had never dreamt that he would neglect her so badly.

'There are ways and means of persuading you to change your mind.' The grimness of his face, the lines scored from nose to mouth, were new, as were the shadows beneath his eyes and the fine lines radiating out from them, the gauntness in his cheeks, the silver hairs at his temple. He had obviously been working hard, pushing himself to his limit. His job was like a terminal illness—always he would work, work, work, and ignore family and friends in the process.

'I don't think even you would resort to brute force,' Sapphire said challengingly, 'and that's the only way you're going to get me out of here. This cottage belongs to a friend, she won't listen to any lies you tell her. I have it for as long as I like.' She swallowed a mouthful of her coffee and glared at him, then grimaced. 'Yuk, you've put sugar in it.'

'You've always taken sugar.'

'Not any more,' she assured him.

He looked at her questioningly. 'In how many other ways have you changed?'

Sapphire's eyes were cold. 'I've discovered I'm quite happy without a man in my life.'

'Without a man?' he picked up quickly, and she knew he was mentally visualising her next-door neighbour.

'You have a smutty mind,' she tossed caustically.

'How could any man resist someone as charming and attractive as you?' he asked in a tone without humour.

'You did a pretty good job of it yourself,' retorted Sapphire. 'The hours and hours I sat in your house alone are unbelievable.'

'Are you suggesting that you spend no time alone now?'

She clenched her lips and gave a tiny shake of her head. 'You'll never understand, will you? Please drink your coffee and go. The very thought that we could get back together and live happily is ludicrous.'

'In other words, you'd rather share your bed with that swine next door than me?' Muscles jerked unsteadily in his jaw and the knuckles on his hand holding the mug grew white. 'Perhaps I ought to remind you, Sapphire, that you're still my wife. I still have as much right to your body as I've ever had.'

Sapphire gave a gasp of disbelief. 'I've heard of men who adopt that attitude,' she scorned. 'I'm afraid they don't rank very high, in my opinion. A piece of paper gives you no rights whatsoever.'

'You're still my wife.'

'In name only.'

'Then we'll have to see about remedying it, won't we?' He moved towards her, and the intent in his eyes was clear.

Sapphire stepped back in desperation. She knew what would happen if he kissed her, if he touched her, even. Her emotions would storm out of control, she would be unable to hide the fact that her body responded to his with all the unbridled passion of a new love. Already feelings were welling up inside her, sensations she had thought long since dead. It was going to be hell until he had gone.

Drake saw the fear in her eyes and misinterpreted it for loathing. With a swift snort of anger he swung away. 'I'll bide my time,' he growled, 'but I'll guarantee this—by the end of a few days you'll be begging me to make love to you.'

Afraid of giving too much away, Sapphire took her coffee over to the window and looked out at the neatly manicured lawn. She had taken great pleasure in restoring the overgrown garden, had developed a feel for it that she had not known she possessed, and with a little help from Robin with the heavy digging—when his back allowed—she now had a garden to be proud of.

She did not realise that Drake had followed her until his hand touched her shoulder. She stiffened but did not turn. 'A pretty garden. Who's responsible for it—Robin?' There was a hardness to his tone and his fingers bit painfully into her skin when he mentioned the other man's name.

'I've done most of it myself,' she told him proudly, desperately trying to ignore the quickening of her senses. The familiar male scent of him was like an aphrodisiac; it aroused and stimulated and made her forget the pain. She wondered if it would always be like this. She wondered if any other man would ever affect her the way Drake did. Or had he spoilt her for anyone else? Was she consigned to loving this one man for the rest of her life—whether they lived apart or not? It was a paralysing thought.

'I didn't know you were interested in gardening.' At Treetops Drake had employed a man to do the garden and Sapphire had never touched it.

'It's a new skill,' she told him.

'It's taken over from your photography? I always knew it was just an excuse to get together with that bastard Colin,' he growled.

Sapphire flashed him a look of scorn. 'You're wrong, Drake. I still take photographs. I'm doing very well at it, as a matter of fact.'

'You mean you're making money out of it?' he asked with a frown.

'That's right,' she answered. 'So your assumption that I came begging for money was way off the mark. I photograph gardens and plants and flowers and trees, et cetera. They seem to sell fairly well.' Which was a modest statement. They sold extremely well. She was fast winning a name for herself as one of the leading photographers in her field—a phenomenon indeed, considering the length of time she had been doing it. It was a very rewarding and satisfying profession, and Sapphire enjoyed it much more than being a secretary.

She did not tell Drake any of this, she had the feeling he wouldn't really be interested, and this hunch was confirmed when he dismissed it as no more than a hobby. 'It's obviously keeping you amused, but you can't really expect me to believe you make enough money out of it to live on—at least not in the lifestyle to which you've been accustomed,' he remarked.

'I manage well enough,' she said stiffly.

He grunted his disbelief and then dismissed the subject entirely. 'I'll fetch my suitcase, then perhaps we can have breakfast together.'

'Your case?' Sapphire swung around, her mouth and eyes wide with astonishment. 'Do you mean to say you actually came here *planning* to stay?'

'Not exactly,' he admitted, 'but I believe in being prepared,' adding with wry humour, 'I wasn't in the Scouts for nothing.'

Sapphire shook her head disbelievingly. 'You still haven't said how you found me.'

His lips quirked. 'You were right, I did follow you. You'd done a very good job of covering up your tracks. Telling your parents you were living in London was a master stroke; it wasted me a whole lot of time.' There was a sudden strong, caustic edge to his tone. 'But you should have known I'd catch up with you one day.'

'They never said you'd been in touch.' Sapphire returned frowningly. She still telephoned home every day, and her mother had not said a word about Drake contacting them, which she found very strange in the circumstances. She was glad her mother had passed on the lie, but even so she could have said something, given her some hint.

'I asked them not to. I knew you'd turn up on my doorstep sooner or later.'

It was said with such confidence that Sapphire looked at him sharply. 'How could you be so sure?'

'Because, my dear wife, I found out how much money meant to you. Wasn't it your ambition to marry a rich man?'

So this was what he had been on about when she turned up at his house. 'I did have such *childish* dreams,' she confessed reluctantly, 'but that——'

'But nothing,' he interjected with a sneer. 'As soon as your sister Louise told me I knew that all I had to do was cut off your allowance. And it worked. It really was remarkably simple.'

'You swine,' snapped Sapphire. 'Your money doesn't interest me. That wasn't the reason I was at Treetops yesterday, and you know it.'

'I know the excuse you gave me.' His light blue eyes were as penetrating as a laser beam. 'But I know what I prefer to believe.'

Sapphire was disgusted with his insinuation and furious with her sister for telling him such nonsense.

'And I think the time has come when we need to sort ourselves out,' he added on a positive note.

'I know exactly what I want to do with the rest of my life,' she told him coldly, 'and it doesn't include you.' He was taking far too much for granted. She did not want him here, she did not want him staying in this cottage, confusing her, unsettling her. It would be far too easy to succumb, to let all the old feelings take over, and where would it end? She would be back to square one.

Admittedly her photography now took her out quite a lot, but she never stayed away overnight. If she did, it would never be for days and days at a time, weekends as well. Drake had been totally unfair, and she had no intention of walking back into the same situation.

His eyes narrowed on hers. 'But it includes Robin, is that what you're saying?'

'I'm saying nothing,' she answered icily. 'If I were a man I'd throw you out, but if you insist on staying then you'll have to sleep on the sofa. You're most definitely not sharing my bed, and there's no other room. I've taken over the second bedroom as a darkroom. Besides, I can't see that talking will do any good; my mind is made up.'

'Then it will be up to me to change your mind, won't it?' Drake fetched his case out of the car and it was reassuringly small, which meant he hadn't planned on staying long, she thought, but it was nevertheless going to be sheer purgatory having him in the house. She was used to wandering around in next to nothing; now she would have to make sure that she was decently covered at all times. Even though he was legally her husband she no longer saw him in that light, and she had no intention of putting temptation in his way.

She put bacon under the grill and set the frying pan on the stove ready for the eggs, and after a few minutes Drake joined her. He filled the tiny kitchen with his presence and it was impossible for her to think straight; she almost burned the bacon and the eggs were crisp at the edges. He looked at her quizzically. 'Your mind was on other things?'

'What do you think?' she snapped. 'The last person in the world I want to share this cottage with is you.'

'If this is an example of the food I'll get,' he said with wry humour, 'it looks as though we'll be eating out most of the time.'

Sapphire merely glanced at him sharply and carried the plates through to the sitting-room, where a drop-leaf table stood against one wall. She rarely used it herself, choosing to balance her plate on her lap, but somehow she couldn't see Drake doing anything so undignified.

They sat opposite each other and his eyes were on her constantly. It reminded Sapphire of that first time he had taken her out for a meal; he had looked at her all the time then and she had felt as though she were melting on the spot. Those same sensations began to flood through her, mind-blowing sensations over which she had no control. Excitement quickened her pulses, her adrenalin ran high, and every bite of food she took tasted like sawdust; swallowing became virtually impossible.

It was an insane situation and one she would have given anything to avoid. This was her husband, the man she loved, who still managed to arouse feelings of a most passionate kind, and yet she wished him a million miles away. With difficulty, by avoiding his eyes, she managed to force the bacon and egg down, and the second her plate was empty she scraped back her chair and stood up.

She thought of telling Drake that she had work to do, some photographs to take; but as he had already found out about the proposed London trip he would know it was a lie. There was no way she could avoid him.

'I'll make some more coffee,' she said thickly, and shot into the kitchen, taking her time, dwelling on the sudden speed with which her past had caught up with her. She had resigned herself to living the rest of her life without Drake, and now here he was planning to spend goodness knew how long with her. She hoped fervently that it was no more than a couple of days. The strain of pretending indifference for any length of time would be intolerable.

'Tell me some more about this guy who lives next door,' said Drake when she returned, and it was clear by the grimness of his mouth that he had been thinking about Robin while she was absent.

'What do you want to know?' she asked crisply, setting the cups down on the table and resuming her seat.

'Is he married?'

Sapphire nodded. Drake's frown deepened. 'But he's a widower,' she clarified quickly.

'He has children?'

'A daughter at college.'

'He knows you're married? Or at least, did he know you were married before I turned up?'

'But of course.'

'So he has no scruples?' They were savage words, hurled at her with the precision of a professional knife-thrower.

'There's nothing going on between Robin and me,' she protested.

'You expect me to believe that?' he asked scornfully. 'It's like asking me to believe white is black. You're forgetting I saw the way he sprang to your protection when he thought I was hassling you.'

Sapphire lifted her shoulders. 'Suit yourself, but I'm not in the habit of lying.'

'Not in normal circumstances, I agree,' he said, 'but these are hardly normal.'

'Then if you're not prepared to accept my word why ask the question?' she demanded sharply.

'I'm a man, Sapphire, I know how men think, the way their minds work. Robin's hardly likely to want you as a platonic friend. The guy would have to be a moron not to be in love with you.'

'That doesn't mean to say that I have to be in love with him.'

'So you're admitting that he does feel something for you?'

'How the hell do I know?' asked Sapphire loudly. 'It's not a subject we've discussed. He's a good neighbour and I don't know what I'd have done without him, but as for anything else I'm afraid it's all in your mind. I hope you're not going to spend every minute interrogating me about Robin?'

'Certainly not. There are other far more important things to discuss, like when are you coming home?'

Sapphire eyed him with cold distaste in her eyes. 'To what—the same sort of loneliness as I left behind? I've built a life for myself here and I'm very happy.' It was an untruth. She was only reasonably happy, or had been until Drake turned up. Now the old turmoil had begun all over again. 'I'm not in love with you any more, Drake,' she lied. 'There would be absolutely no point in my coming back.'

CHAPTER FOUR

DRAKE'S light blue eyes were like glittering shards of ice, his whole body suddenly tense. 'Do you mean that, Sapphire? Are you honestly saying you don't love me?'

She nodded, making herself look at him, hiding the hurt that tore through her like a well-aimed bullet. She could not see why he was so uptight when he was the one who had been cheating on their marriage. If anyone had fallen out of love it was him. 'All I want,' she said quietly, 'is to be able to get on with my life.'

'I have no intention of divorcing you,' he told her.

'Then I shall divorce you,' she said flatly. 'I'll wait the statutory two years and do it myself.'

A black eyebrow rose. 'You're obviously not fully conversant with the law. Two years with consent by the other partner, yes, but without that consent you have to wait five. Are you prepared for that? Five long years, Sapphire. Five years when you're not free to marry anyone else. It sounds like a life sentence, doesn't it? Is your friend Robin prepared to wait that long?'

The dismay on her face was clear for him to see, and he laughed harshly, and without waiting for her response he stood up. 'I had planned to sit and talk, but with the risk of your friend interrupting again I think a change of plan is in order. We'll go out. Change into a dress, something pretty and feminine. You know I hate you in jeans.'

Resenting him giving orders, Sapphire said bitterly, 'Why should I do what you ask when this is *my* home?'

'I remember the time when you'd do anything to please me,' Drake tossed back scathingly. 'Have things changed so much?'

Sapphire lifted her shoulders in what she hoped was an indifferent shrug. 'You should know, you're the one who's to blame for all this.' Without looking at him she collected the crockery and took it into the kitchen.

'I'll wash up while you change,' he said quickly.

Sapphire hid her surprise. This wasn't the Drake she knew. He had always been far too busy or far too tired to help her; there had never been any periods of shared domesticity. This was certainly a new side to her husband, and if that was what he wanted to do then she was willing to let him get on with it.

The dress she chose to wear was a relatively new one; a simple full-skirted style in lemon-coloured crinkle cotton. The bodice dipped low at the back and showed off the flattering tan she had acquired while spending hours taking photographs out of doors.

She slipped her feet into a pair of medium-heeled sandals which, though elegant, were also suitable for walking. It was difficult knowing exactly what to wear when she did not know where Drake was taking her. It was the busy season in Cornwall and everywhere was packed with holidaymakers—it was not Sapphire's favourite time of year. She loved it in the early spring when buds were bursting and daffodils blooming and it was still too early in the season for trippers.

She was soon to discover, however, that there were still a few secret places which the intrepid holidaymakers had not found. Drake seemed to know every nook and cranny. The scenery got starker and the roads quieter, and eventually they turned off into a narrow, leafy lane which grew narrower and narrower until it was nothing more than a track with grass growing along the middle.

The thick hedgerows were vibrant with wild flowers, pink foxgloves and campion, white yarrow, bracken, thistles, brilliant red poppies. And then suddenly, quite unexpectedly, they came upon a cluster of houses huddled together in the shelter of a valley.

Drake stopped the car and they got out, and he led her towards one of the cottages. Sapphire looked at him in some surprise. The old woman who opened the door took one look at his face, then smiled broadly. 'Well, mercy me, what a pleasure this is.'

He enveloped her warmly in his arms. 'Don't I always turn up like a bad penny?'

'But not often enough,' she reprimanded, though there was no real censure in her voice. She was tiny and bent and must have been about eighty, but her voice was strong and she looked enquiringly at Sapphire. 'Is this——'

'Yes, this is my wife,' said Drake quietly, and somewhat proudly, Sapphire thought. 'At last I've brought her to see you.'

She wanted to yell out that they no longer lived together, but Drake was already pulling her forward. 'Sapphire, I'd like you to meet my grandmother, my own flesh-and-blood granny, known to everyone as Granny Oakland. We lost touch for a while after my mother divorced Eric, but now we're the best of friends.'

'That no-good daughter of mine,' muttered the old woman bitterly. 'I haven't seen her since she split up with Eric Willows, and nor do I want to. I thought she'd taken Drake with her until he turned up one day and told me the whole sorry story. But what are we doing talking on the doorstep? Come along in.'

It was a cheerful, comfortable cottage which, despite her age, Drake's grandmother kept neat and tidy and spotlessly clean. They sat down, and she produced a pot of tea which she poured into pretty yellow cups. 'Now tell me all about yourselves,' she said. 'How long have you been married now? It's very naughty of you, Drake, to have left it so long before bringing Sapphire to see me.'

'Two and a half years,' supplied Sapphire, 'but we've been separated,' she added quickly. She did not want him telling his grandmother any half-truths.

'Oh, dear.' A distressed frown added to the patchwork of wrinkles on the woman's face. 'But now you're back together?' she assumed with a thankful smile. 'Oh, Drake, I don't want you going the same way as your mother. Marriages aren't made in heaven, we all know that—they need working on.'

To Sapphire's surprise he nodded. 'That's exactly what we're doing, Gran.'

Sapphire looked at him in sharp protest, but he gave her a faint warning frown, and she supposed it would do no harm. As he apparently did not see his grandmother often the woman would be content thinking that his marriage was working out.

'Have you any children?' was the old lady's next discerning question.

Drake's abrupt, 'No!' startled his grandmother, then she sighed resignedly. 'I know you've seen the other side of the story, my son, I know your childhood wasn't a happy one, but I'm sure that wouldn't be the case with your own children. Not all women are like Elizabeth. How she could walk off and leave you I'll never know; I'm sure Sapphire would never do a thing like that. Now why don't you show Sapphire our beautiful valley while I prepare you some lunch?'

'We're not staying,' said Drake at once. 'I don't want to put you to any trouble.'

'Nonsense,' said his grandmother tartly. 'It's not often you come to see me. I'd be most hurt if you left without having something to eat.'

Drake lifted his shoulders in an easy shrug, his smile warm and encompassing. 'OK, Gran, you win!' But once they were outdoors the smile disappeared. 'She's quite a woman, my grandmother.'

Sapphire nodded. 'She's lovely. I wish you'd brought me to see her before.' He had mentioned her, had said often that he ought to visit her, but somehow he never found the time. The same as he hadn't found time for her! How he had managed to take a few days off now she did not know. 'It's very remiss of you, Drake, to neglect her so badly when she's so obviously fond of you.'

'She's in my thoughts,' he said, as if that were enough.

'Has she really never seen her daughter from the day she left you with Eric?'

He nodded grimly. 'That's right. She can be a very hard woman when she wants, can my grandmother. I can quite believe that if Elizabeth turned up right now she wouldn't even let her in the house; the same as I want nothing to do with her either. I was eight years old when it happened, and I was very distressed for a long time.'

'How old were you when you made contact with your grandmother again?' asked Sapphire.

Drake thought for a moment. 'It was about fifteen years ago, so I must have been eighteen. For ten years she'd had no word of me or Elizabeth. It was a very emotional reunion.'

'It must have broken her heart to have a daughter who was so casual about her own child.'

'It broke my heart to be left behind,' he muttered. 'I couldn't understand why my mother didn't love me any more.' His face was haunted by dark shadows, and Sapphire almost felt sorry for him—almost, but not quite. He had hurt her too, though she was sure he did not realise exactly how much.

To her surprise the valley led into a tiny but enchanting, sheltered cove, completely deserted, the blue waters of the Atlantic lapping at the golden sand. It was an unreal, beautiful spot that she had never known existed, and would never have found if Drake hadn't brought her.

'It's not on any map,' he said in answer to her unspoken question. 'As far as the world's concerned it doesn't exist.' High, battered cliffs rose on each side, making it invisible except from out at sea.

'It's like something out of a storybook,' she said, enchanted, her animosity for the moment forgotten. 'The water's so inviting—how I'd love to swim.'

'What's to stop you?' he asked drily.

She turned to him, a look of alarm on her face. 'Skinny-dipping is not one of my fantasies. I'd have brought my swimsuit if you'd told me we were coming here.'

'I wouldn't see anything I haven't seen before,' Drake reminded her grimly.

That was very true, thought Sapphire, but stripping off in front of Drake was the last thing she planned to do. It was bad enough that he still had the power to disturb her without putting herself at a disadvantage. Her heart raced at the very thought, and she turned away and pretended an interest in a fern-like plant that was growing against a boulder. What a pity she had not brought her camera. She had come prepared for nothing at all, and here were all these marvellous things just waiting to be captured on film.

When she straightened she was alarmed to discover Drake standing close behind her, so close in fact that her body brushed his, creating a flurry of sensation through each and every nerve. He made no attempt to move away, and she saw the glitter of desire in his eyes.

Drawing in a swift, instinctive, defensive breath, she stepped sideways, but Drake's arm shot out to stop her and before she knew what was happening she was imprisoned against the rock-hardness of his body. 'I think,' he muttered thickly, 'that it's time we found out exactly what your feelings for me are.'

Sapphire felt the hurried throb of his heart, the heat of desire that coursed through his veins. She ought to have known he had something like this in mind. She ought to have known he wouldn't seek her out and then ignore the sexual awareness that had always run high between them. Neither time nor separation had dimmed it, and she knew it was imperative that she escape now before she unwittingly revealed the true state of her feelings.

But it was already too late. His dark head lowered, his lips brushed the soft skin of her throat, burning, assaulting, awakening. Her cry was a mixture of pain and pleasure. She had never forgotten how sensual he was, but she did not remember this intensity of feeling, this very real need that he was able to incite without even trying. She was in danger of drowning in the mire of her heightened emotions.

And when he began to kiss her, when his lips touched hers, she no longer had the will-power to reject him. Her heart beat frantically and she wanted this moment to go on forever. She wanted to forget that she had ever walked out on him. She wanted them to be one again, husband and wife, loving and needing, never apart.

It's insanity, muttered a little voice inside her, it won't be a proper marriage. Always his job will come first, making money is top on his list of priorities. You must put a stop to it right now.

But it was not so easy. As his kiss deepened and became more possessive she opened her lips and her arms snaked around him, her movements involuntarily following past patterns. And she knew with a sickening feeling that there was not a thing she could do about it. The time they had spent apart made no difference; she was as much under his spell as she had ever been.

His hands moved with skilled, erotic strokes over her back, sliding her dress from her shoulders and cupping her vulnerable, aching breasts. Sapphire whimpered her pleasure again, and her throat arched as her head fell back. The times she had dreamed of Drake doing this to her, the times her body had ached for him. It all felt so right.

And when he lowered his head, when he took first one and then the other sensitised nipple into his mouth her excitement knew no bounds. Her body moved with unconscious eroticism against his, her fingers threading through the wiry thickness of his hair. Her whole body throbbed and a threatened dizziness promised to knock her off her feet.

It was not until her dress fell to her ankles and his fingers touched the lace edge of her panties that some sort of sanity returned. 'No, Drake, no...' The words came out in an unsteady gush.

'Yes, Sapphire, yes,' he said thickly. 'It's too late for protests. I know you want this as much as me.'

'No, I don't—I don't!' she cried, looking up into the clear blue of his eyes. In them she saw a flare of triumph and suddenly realised that she had fallen right into his trap. He had set out to seduce her, to see if the fires were still alight inside her body, and she had given him his answer as clearly as if she had said she still loved him.

'Little liar.' Drake's lips curved in a derogatory smile. 'You think I can't tell what you're thinking and feeling?'

'OK, so you still affect me physically,' Sapphire snapped, 'but there's nothing else, no other feelings. I refuse to let you grope me as though I'm your plaything.'

His face became masklike, his hooded eyes glittering like slivers of silver. 'I take offence at that remark. I was doing nothing that you didn't want me to do.'

'Like hell you weren't,' she stormed. 'I never even wanted to come out with you. You've done nothing but ride roughshod over me all day.' She bent to retrieve her dress, to pull it back on over her naked, all too vulnerable body, but he was quicker. He snatched it away from her questing fingers and stepped back a pace.

Sapphire was furious. It had never seemed wrong standing undressed in front of her husband when they lived together, but now, somehow, it was positively indecent. The trouble was she had nowhere to hide—except the sea! With a cry that held both pain and anger she turned from him and ran.

For the first few seconds the water felt cold and took her breath away, but soon she got used to it and after a few strokes began to enjoy the feel of the silky water against her naked flesh. She refused to look back at the shore. She did not want to see Drake watching her, mocking her, waiting for her to come out. This was something she had not thought about when she ran headlong into the water; now she realised that all she had done was put off the evil moment.

It came as quite a surprise, therefore, when he swam up behind her and pulled her back against him. It was a wild sensation, a completely new experience, even more so when he turned her to face him and with his hands about her waist lifted her high out of the water before letting her slide slowly down the length of his body.

Despite the coolness of the water she was on fire, sensations sizzling inside her such as she had never felt before. There was a merciless grin on Drake's face as though he knew exactly what he was doing to her. He made a game of swimming around her, but always there were undertones of sexuality; the way he touched her, the way he brushed his body against hers, the way his mouth tasted her skin. It was eroticism personified. At one stage he pulled down her panties and let the tide carry them away, and this time she was unable to stop him. Never before had she known him in such a playful mood, and she did not think she could take much more of it without responding.

And then suddenly it was over. He took her hand and they waded towards the shore, and Sapphire pretended it was perfectly normal to walk naked across a beach. Drake wore nothing either, striding along with the same easy gait that he used when in his business suits. There had always been something of the animal in him, in his loping stride and powerful, muscular grace, but it had never been more evident than at this moment.

The sun was strong and hot and began to dry their bodies even before they reached their pile of clothes, which Drake had neatly folded on a boulder, but when Sapphire would have pulled on her dress he stopped her. 'Wait until you're properly dry.'

She turned wide, protesting eyes in his direction, but was stopped from speaking when his mouth came down on hers. She was pulled against the taut hardness of his cool, damp body, and her heightened feelings took off on a stampede of their own.

He had the power to drive her crazy, to make her arch her body into his and exult in the feel of his manhood against her. So long it had been, so long. All sane thoughts fled. This man was her husband, and she wanted him so much, so very, very much.

Heat and fire coursed through her trembling limbs. Her heart had never throbbed so loudly or painfully. She clung to him, her fingernails raking the firm skin of his back, her mouth opening willingly to his, accepting his probing tongue, enjoying the taste of him, his mastery, his dominance. In that instant whatever he wanted she wanted too.

His hands moved possessively, feeling the shape of her, reacquainting himself with every contour, with each throbbing, sensitive pulse. His lips seared her skin as they trailed down the aching column of her throat to her heavy, swollen breasts, tormenting each nipple in turn before moving lower, ever lower.

She was leaning back against the cliff-face now, oblivious of the rocky protusions digging into her back, conscious only of Drake's lips and tongue and hands which were robbing her of sane thought, creating new and incredible sensations.

Out here in the open, with the breeze playing on her skin, she felt not only vulnerable but wanton too, a deep, primitive urge welling up inside her to meet like with like. She pressed her lips to his shoulders, tasting the salty tang of the sea, running her hands over his body as he had over hers, and when he straightened in front of her she touched her tongue and teeth to his nipples and felt him shudder from head to toe.

His eyes were glazed with desire, his fingers hard and almost brutal as he pulled her fiercely against him, his chest heaving as he fought for control. 'Sapphire,

Sapphire,' he muttered, 'you do know what's going to happen?'

She nodded, her eyes mirroring the pain in his. Who cared at this moment? All she wanted was fulfilment. The aching need inside her could only be assuaged by this one man. For the moment everything else was forgotten except this craving for Drake, the feeling of being at one with him that had been absent from her life for six long months.

When his hands moved to touch the most secret part of her, found her moist and ready and hungry for love, he drew in his breath in a swift hiss of pleasure. 'Oh, my love...' he groaned.

At that moment sanity returned, sanity and a sickness in the pit of her stomach. He wanted her now, but how often had it been his mistress who lay in his arms? How often had he wanted this other woman? Which of them did he love, or neither? Was he interested in sex alone? Was this what motivated him? Sapphire tensed and tried to pull away, and he frowned and said harshly, 'What's wrong?'

'This is wrong,' she said huskily. 'You and me. I must have been crazy to go this far. Please let me go.'

For a few throbbing seconds she thought he was going to refuse, that he was going to make love to her anyway and to hell with what she wanted. He held her shoulders so tightly that she knew she would be bruised tomorrow, and the torment in his eyes was terrible to see. And then a shutter came down, blanked off everything he was thinking and feeling, and she was free, free of his thrusting body, but not free of the pulsating need still inside her.

He picked up her dress and threw it at her with vicious movements, then pulled on his own clothes with demonic speed. Without a word or even waiting to see whether she was ready he strode back towards his grandmother's cottage.

Even though Sapphire knew she had done the right thing she felt oddly guilty. She had actively encouraged Drake and then cut him off when he was almost beyond himself with need. Not that he didn't deserve it, the swine, after the way he had treated her. The thought of another woman sharing this side of him made jealousy rise up in her throat like bile, and she was glad she had stopped him—glad, glad, glad.

Once dressed, she followed the path Drake had stormed along a few minutes earlier, surprised to find him waiting a short distance from the cottage. There was something dark and menacing in his eyes which made her tense up again, and she halted and looked at him, trying her hardest not to show that she felt intimidated. *Intimidated*! By her own husband! It was crazy—and yet that was how she felt.

'You needn't think I don't intend to finish what was started down there on the beach,' he growled. 'That's the first time you've ever said no to me, and it sure as hell is going to be the last. Remember that, dear wife.'

The grating tones of his voice shivered over her skin and she hugged her arms across her chest, feeling cold all over again. Nevertheless she eyed him calmly. 'You're forgetting that as far as I'm concerned we're no longer man and wife.'

An angry glitter sparked from his eyes. 'Oh, yes, we are. Until the day a piece of paper is signed to say that we're not, then you're mine. Never let go of that fact, Sapphire.'

She shook her head in violent disbelief, causing the wet strands of her hair to stick to her cheeks. Before she could lift a hand to move them Drake was doing it for her, his fingers gentle, total concentration on his face.

The back of his hand brushed her skin, and he somehow turned the simple action into a sensual movement, making her ache with longing all over again. It was hard not to take hold of his hand and press it to her lips.

'I don't want my grandmother to know there's anything wrong,' he muttered.

'I'm not an actress,' she snapped, snatching away from his tormenting fingers. Dear heaven, it was going to be sheer hell until he went back home. What a fatal mistake she had made going anywhere near Treetops.

'But you'll do your best?' he insisted on a harder note.

Sapphire swallowed and nodded, and with that he had to be satisfied, but there was no smile on her face when they went into the house.

'You've been swimming?' Granny Oakland looked at Sapphire's wet hair and immediately handed her a towel. 'The bathroom's through there. Go and wash that salt off your skin.'

Sapphire was glad to make her escape into the little room that had been built on to the back of the cottage. She could hear the murmur of their voices, though not what they were saying, and she wondered whether Drake was confessing that they had been swimming in the nude. Even so, she somehow felt that the older woman wouldn't be shocked.

What a day it was turning out to be. When she had awoken this morning it was with the thought that she was going to London with Robin. If anyone had told her she would be swimming naked in a private little cove with her husband, and that she would be very close to him making love to her, she would have called them a liar. It was amazing how one's life could change within the space of a few seconds.

Ten minutes later, clean and dry, her hair brushed neatly, she joined Drake and his grandmother in the kitchen. He smiled at her warmly, as though there was nothing at all wrong. 'Feel better now, darling?'

She nodded, but avoided his eyes, glad his grandmother did not know she was completely naked beneath the dress. It made her feel too vulnerable, too easily aroused, and Drake knew it—she could tell by the way he looked at her. To hide her tension she sniffed the aroma of baking. 'Mmm, something smells good. I hadn't realised how hungry I was.'

'Steak and kidney pie,' said the old lady, 'though I'm afraid the meat's out of a tin. If I'd know you were coming it would have been fresh, of course—but the vegetables are straight out of the garden. If you're ready I'll dish it up. Drake says he's going to wait until he gets home for his bath.'

Home to her cottage, not his own house, thought Sapphire bitterly. He had no right calling it home. Even though she knew the charade was for Gran's benefit she did not like it, and she pursed her lips, though she changed it to a smile when she saw the old woman look sharply at her.

Although Sapphire did her best to pretend there was nothing wrong it was an impossible situation. Her awareness of Drake hammered continuously along her nerve streams, and his constant endearments and the softness in his voice when he spoke to her all contributed to the unrest in her body. How could she not respond? And yet she could not forget his threat outside, and it worried her. There was no way she was going to let him make love to her. By amusing himself with another woman he had as effectively put an end to their marriage as she had when walking out.

The pie was delicious, the pastry golden and mouthwatering, and they both did justice to it. Sapphire ate slowly, trying to put off the moment when they would be taking their leave, and she was alone with Drake, but eventually the meal was over and Gran was clearing the table.

'I'll help you wash up,' said Sapphire, eager to escape Drake for a few minutes, and the old woman nodded and smiled.

'That's very kind of you.'

But once in the kitchen Sapphire wished she hadn't offered. She had not expected Granny Oakland to be so perceptive. 'There's still something wrong with your marriage, isn't there?' the old lady asked the instant they were alone.

Not sure what to say or how much Gran had guessed, Sapphire shrugged. 'We're not exactly back on the same footing, but it's early days yet.' She would keep up the pretence for Drake's grandmother's sake, not for Drake himself. Once they were away from here she would tell him to get out of her life and stay out.

'So what went wrong in the first place?' Gran was filling the washing-up bowl with hot water and did not look at Sapphire as she spoke.

'He spent more time at work than he did with me,' she said, and something in her tone made the other woman look sharply around.

'It's not a sin wishing to provide for your home and family.' There was gentle censure in her voice.

But it is a sin to commit adultery, thought Sapphire bitterly. She wouldn't upset the old lady by telling her this, though. 'He took me away from my friends and family and then left me alone in the house,' she said, trying hard not to sound reproachful. 'I didn't mind during the day, there was plenty to do, but he stayed out most nights, and then it got to the stage when he was away weekends as well. I couldn't take that.'

'And now you're back together is he any better?' Granny Oakland had turned back to the sink and was busy washing dishes with an old-fashioned string mop on a wooden handle.

Sapphire wasn't sure how to answer that. She had no idea whether Drake still lived out of a suitcase or not. 'He—he's making an effort,' she conceded.

'My husband and I had our ups and downs the same as anyone else, but we lived through them, and I think I can safely say we were still in love with each other on the day he died when he was seventy-two.' It was an injunction that married life wasn't all a bed of roses.

Sapphire picked up a plate and began polishing it dry, not really knowing what to say to these confidences.

'It's easy to see that Drake loves you very much,' the old lady went on.

Drake loved her? That was the joke of the century. He wouldn't have treated her so casually if he did. His grandmother was definitely wrong there.

'And if he works a little too hard at times it's all for your sake. He's turned out surprisingly well, considering the way he was treated as a child. How my daughter could leave him like that, I don't know. Rosemarie is much more of a mother to him than Elizabeth ever was. I haven't seen her since she split with Eric, and I don't think I want to. I'm not proud of saying that, Sapphire, it breaks my heart when I think how she turned out, but if she's so uncaring then it's best that she and I don't meet.'

'I'm sorry about your daughter,' said Sapphire huskily. 'I know how you must feel.' She wondered where Elizabeth lived now and whether she had ever married again and whether she ever thought about Drake—or whether he was a part of her past she did not care to remember. Sapphire could not understand how a woman could reject her own flesh and blood. It didn't make sense. It had crucified her to lose her own baby, and she knew that had it lived she would have loved it for ever.

'It's Drake you should feel sorry for, knowing his own mother is out there somewhere and doesn't care a fig about him.'

'He doesn't need my sympathy,' said Sapphire, her voice unconsciously cold.

'You sound bitter, child.' Again the old woman turned and looked at her. 'You don't approve? You think he should forgive his mother?'

'No,' said Sapphire at once. 'I'd probably feel the same in his situation.'

Granny Oakland looked at her shrewdly. 'Don't let him down, my dear. I wouldn't like to see his life shattered a second time. Being abandoned was a traumatic experience for him; it didn't leave him with a very good impression of loving parents and a happily married life.'

'I'll try not to.' Sapphire's tones were husky. She made sense, this smart old woman. She had given her an insight into what Drake had suffered and felt, but it still did not help the fact that the reason for their break-up was entirely Drake's fault. It had nothing at all to do with his unhappy childhood, except perhaps that it was the rejection he felt when he was young that had made him want to make something of his life now, perhaps make him independent of other people. Was that why he found it difficult to settle down? Ought she to have realised that if he had not got married by the age of thirty-one there had to be a very strong reason?

When they rejoined Drake Sapphire could tell he was eager to be gone, and it was only a matter of minutes before he stood up and suggested they make a move.

'Don't be so long in coming to see me next time,' his grandmother scolded, at the same time as she gave him a warm kiss. And to Sapphire, 'If he's too busy to bring you come on your own. You'll always be welcome.'

'Thank you,' said Sapphire, 'I'll remember that.' But she doubted whether she would ever accept the invitation. There would be too many probing questions, and no matter how she tried she would never be able to pull the wool over this woman's eyes.

Drake made a great show of helping her into the car, but Sapphire wasn't fooled. She knew it was all put on for his grandmother's benefit. Nevertheless she could not dispute the fact that his presence was overpowering, that his nearness stifled her. The whole day had served to make her more and more aware of him, and the feelings would not go away.

But even worse than that was her feeling of defencelessness. It was the lack of undies that did it, and Drake would not be human if he did not feel aroused too. It did not bode well for when they got back to the cottage. She had hoped the quiet interlude with his grandmother would put an end to his desire, but it was not so; she could sense the passion riding high inside him. The last hour or two had been nothing more than a brief respite.

CHAPTER FIVE

'WHAT were you and my grandmother talking about so intently?' asked Drake as he drove away from the cottage. 'I thought I heard my name mentioned.'

'So you were listening?' Sapphire's tone was unintentionally sharp.

'Not really. I'm not the type of person who eavesdrops on other people's conversations.'

'And I'm not the type of person who discloses them,' she snapped.

'She's a grand old lady,' he said with a private smile. 'I've neglected her lately—I must make sure I don't do it again.'

'She's not the only person you've neglected,' retorted Sapphire

Had she looked she would have seen the tautness in his jaw, but she was staring straight ahead and only felt the silence. 'I intend changing all that.'

She did look at him then, a startled expression on her face. 'You mean you're actually going to give yourself some free time?'

Drake nodded.

'I don't believe it,' she said scornfully. 'You're too involved in your damn work to take time off. Oh, I believe you're full of good intentions, but it won't last. You need to have your finger constantly on every pulse.'

He didn't deny it, and she knew he couldn't because it was true, but what he did say was, 'I want you to give our marriage another go.'

'You mean you'll be the perfect husband for a few weeks, or a few months even, until someone loses an order and you decide they can't manage without you. Oh, yes, I know what it will be like. I had two years of it, don't forget. A leopard never changes its spots.'

'Damn you, Sapphire,' he hissed. 'I don't think that was called for.'

'Don't you?' she retorted. 'You weren't on the receiving end. You can promise as much as you like, I know it won't work. I'm not coming back to you, Drake, it's as simple as that.' There were other reasons, such as wanting children when he didn't, but there was no point in telling him that.

'You can't deny that your body still craves mine.' His hand came down on her leg as he spoke, stroking, inciting, and a whole flood of out-of-control sensations rushed shamelessly through her.

'No,' she confessed reluctantly, 'I can't deny it, but I don't have to give in to it.'

'Because you keep telling yourself you're in love with that bastard Robin?' he snorted in sudden anger. 'It was because of him you stopped me earlier, wasn't it? A sudden bout of misplaced conscience. Let me tell you something, Sapphire, if you were in love with him and not me then you wouldn't feel anything for me at all. It's not dead, what we had going for us. In fact, it's very much alive, and I intend making sure it stays that way. If you won't come home to me then I shall just have to move in with you. It's as simple as that.'

Sapphire could not believe she was hearing him correctly, she could not believe he would stay in the tiny cottage permanently. 'It wouldn't work,' she rapped. 'I have my work, you have yours, and don't tell me you'd be back every night, because I know you wouldn't.'

'You're not giving me much choice.'

'No,' she spat, 'I'm giving you one option—get away from me and stay away.' Save her peace of mind. The very thought of Drake living in her rented cottage caused turmoil in her heart.

They were out of the lanes now and back on the main roads, which were busy with holiday traffic, fortunately needing his full attention. Sapphire was happy with the silence. She did not want to argue any more about what they should or should not do. She still felt as though she were walking a tightrope, every nerve in her body taut and yet exhilarated at the same time.

It was amazing the power he wielded over her. It was more formidable than ever, dangerously so; arousing, exciting, exhilarating, demanding; sending her into a frenzy of emotions that warred within her until she did not know which way to turn.

She let her head fall back on the seat and closed her eyes, but he still wouldn't go away. The potent male scent of him was strong in her nostrils; he was like a drug, and she was addicted to him whether she liked it or not.

In one way it was a relief when they reached the cottage in Lanreath; in another it was the beginning of a different sort of nightmare. How was she going to stop him from staying indefinitely? How, when he was so determined that they should once again live together as man and wife?

Robin was leaving his house as they pulled up outside, and he looked unsmilingly from Sapphire to Drake and back again. She went over to him and put her hand on his arm. 'I'll explain it all when I get the chance,' she said.

'I can't see that there's much to explain,' he said. 'It looks to me as though you've made it up with your husband. I'm happy for you.' He tried to smile, but it was more of a grimace, and when Drake called to Sapphire Robin turned away and walked down the street.

'Need you make it so obvious that you prefer him to me?' growled Drake when they were indoors.

Sapphire glared and said nothing. Let him jump to whatever conclusions he liked. Robin was a good friend and she did not like to see him unhappy. She had known all along that he thought more of her than she did him, and it was clear he was upset because her husband had turned up. She must tell him the truth as soon as she possibly could. There was no reason at all why they couldn't continue their friendship.

'I'll just have to make sure you keep well away from him,' Drake muttered darkly as he made his way into the kitchen and filled the kettle.

He's acting as though he already lives here, thought Sapphire irritably, and she longed to snatch it from him, but she knew the sort of reaction it would get. Instead she stood and watched him as he had watched her earlier that morning. It was doubtful, though, whether he felt the same unease. In fact he seemed perfectly at home, even whistling softly to himself as he reached out cups and saucers and milk from the refrigerator.

'You have a nerve,' she spat, unable to keep her temper under control any longer. 'This is my kitchen, you know.'

'Ours, unless you come back with me,' he reminded her with a wolfish smile.

'You're insane!'

'You're beautiful.'

Light blue eyes met dark blue, and for a few seconds nothing else existed except this man. The tension was intolerable, and with a cry that sounded almost like desperation Sapphire ran from the kitchen and up the stairs to her own bedroom, where she shut the door and leaned back against it, her heart thudding fit to burst.

It was crazy feeling like this, letting him get through to her so easily. Why couldn't she be strong? Why couldn't she stand up to him and ignore every attempt he made to stir the senses he knew were simmering just below the surface? And by running up here she had told him even more clearly how she felt.

Eventually her heartbeats returned to normal, and she was summoning up the courage to go back downstairs when her eyes alighted on a suitcase thrown on top of her wardrobe. *Drake's* suitcase! She hurriedly opened her wardrobe, and there, at the opposite end to the dress she had taken out earlier, which accounted for the fact that she hadn't seen them, were shirts, a jacket, and two pairs of trousers. It could mean only one thing. Drake intended sleeping with her tonight.

Angrily she gathered them up and burst back into the kitchen. 'I believe these are yours?' she said coldly.

'Of course,' Drake answered evenly. 'You knew I'd brought some clothes with me. What's wrong?'

'Where you put them is what's wrong,' she snapped, not deceived by his innocence for one second.

'There was nowhere to hang them downstairs.'

'And so you thought you'd use *my* wardrobe?' Sapphire countered smartly. 'You weren't by any chance planning to use *my* bed as well?'

He smiled. 'The thought did cross my mind. The sofa doesn't look all that comfortable, not for someone of my size.'

'Well, that's just too bad.' Her tone was filled with biting sarcasm. 'Because there's no way you're sharing with me.' She took his stuff out to the sitting-room and tossed it on to the couch. 'If you're not content with sleeping down here then you can get out,' she said sharply as she returned to the kitchen. 'It's as simple as that.'

He did not answer. He finished pouring the tea, and Sapphire felt sure he was deliberately prolonging the silence to make her feel uncomfortable—and he was succeeding! She could have quite happily knocked the cups off the counter and ordered him out. In fact, she did not know why she wasn't doing it. He couldn't walk in here and do as he liked—this was her house, the only people who came in were invited by her, and Drake was definitely not welcome.

So why was she being so weak? Why hadn't she thrown him out long before now? Was it because she was still in love with him? Did she subconsciously want him to stay, no matter what she told herself? No, of course she didn't. She wanted him out, and she wanted him out now.

'Well,' she asked angrily, feet apart, arms akimbo, 'are you going?'

'I think you know the answer to that as well as me,' Drake answered with yet another slow smile. 'I really don't know why you're kicking up such a fuss.'

'Because you and I are no longer an item. I live here, you live at Treetops.'

'And you're content with that?' His eyes were narrowed on her face as he waited for her answer.

'It's worked very well up till now,' she answered coldly. 'At least I'm making something of my life instead of looking after your house and waiting dutifully for you to come home every night—even though you never did,' she added caustically.

'I always phoned, I always apologised, I always explained.'

'Oh, yes, and you always bought me presents; beautiful gifts of jewellery and flowers and clothes, anything you could think of to pacify your conscience,' she spat, 'but that wasn't what I wanted—I wanted *you*,

Drake, nothing else. In the end I decided that if I was going to be lonely I'd be lonely on my own.'

'And were you?'

'What? Lonely?'

'Yes.'

She lifted her shoulders. 'To begin with.' In truth, she had missed Drake more than she had thought possible. Even when he was away from home a lot there had always been the chance that he would return unexpectedly. The thought that she would never see him again, that they would never share the same bed, had made her go cold inside every time she thought about it.

'To begin with?' he snarled. 'Until you became friendly with that bastard next door, is that what you're saying?'

Sapphire drew in a swift angry breath. 'Let's leave Robin out of this. I've told you, there's nothing between us, we're just good friends.'

'Just good friends,' he sneered. 'I've heard that before. I personally don't think it's possible for a man and woman to have a platonic relationship.'

'You mean *you* don't find it possible,' retorted Sapphire scathingly. 'I can well believe that. Your lady *friend* is the reason you never came home at night. Don't think I don't know about her, because I do.'

Drake's head jerked and he eyed her in shocked surprise. 'Ah, so now we're getting to the bottom of the matter. You think I've been seeing another woman—that's why you ran out on me? May I ask what gave you that impression?'

Sapphire shivered at the savage fury blazing from his eyes. It would appear that Hélène hadn't told him that she'd telephoned; a misguided sense of loyalty, perhaps? Probably the girl was half in love with him herself. 'Let it suffice that I know,' she snapped.

'You mean you jumped to conclusions?' Angry eyes seared into her. 'Entirely erroneous ones, as it happens.'

Jumped, when he'd actually been seen in a London hotel? My goodness me, Sapphire thought, who was he trying to fool? If he had fallen out of love with her so quickly then she was well rid of him. Not that it didn't hurt, not that she hadn't wondered for long hour after long hour what had gone wrong, what *she* had done wrong, why Drake preferred another woman. 'As are yours about me and Robin,' she riposted. 'So *if* I was wrong then that makes us quits.'

'But you're not at all sure that you were wrong, is that what you're suggesting?' he asked icily.

'I only have your word,' she retorted.

'As I have yours that Robin means nothing to you. Now, I suggest we quit this futile conversation before we come to blows. Drink your tea, it's getting cold.'

Sapphire picked up the cup, but her hands were trembling so badly that she put it down again quickly. 'I don't want it, and I don't want you here either.'

'Then that's just too bad,' he sneered, 'because I have no intention at all of leaving until you agree to come home with me.' He folded his arms across his muscular chest, and there was challenge in his blue eyes as he looked at her.

Sapphire was in a quandary. She knew he meant what he said, but she was equally determined not to go with him. How did she get him out, though? Phone the police? She did not want to do that; she did not want to involve anyone else. This was a personal matter between her and Drake. It was up to her to find a way of resolving it.

'I'm not coming back, Drake, no matter what you say,' she said with quiet determination. 'Stay here if you must, but you'll be wasting your time—and how *will* your men get on without you?' She deliberately injected a note of derision into her voice. 'Don't you have to be there all the time to make sure everything's running smoothly? Isn't it essential that you're in on everything?'

A muscle jerked in his jaw and for just a moment anger sparked in his eyes, then it was gone, and there was no expression whatsoever on his face. 'My business is doing well.'

'Good, I'm pleased for you.' Sapphire kept her tone pleasant but cool.

'I did tell you I wouldn't be working such long hours for ever.'

'Of course you did.'

'Dammit, Sapphire, do you have to be so sarcastic?' The fury was back in his eyes.

'I'm merely speaking the truth.' Her chin was high, her eyes very bright.

'I can see we have a lot of talking to do. Things are not as they were, Sapphire.'

Her heart gave a little leap, but she kept her voice cool. 'You're working regular hours?'

'Not strictly,' he confessed.

'You still stay away overnight?'

'On occasions.'

'As I thought,' she snapped. 'Nothing's changed—it never will. You're a workaholic, Drake. It's too late to think we'll ever get back on the same footing. The harm's been done. I want a husband who sleeps in my bed at night, not someone else's.'

If she could have foreseen the savagery that bunched Drake's muscles and turned his eyes to lethal weapons Sapphire would have bit back the words, but it was difficult not to be caustic when she'd been hurt so much.

'Enough of these accusations,' he raged. 'If you're going to throw things like that at me then I want concrete evidence. Who am I supposed to have been sleeping with? Is it hearsay? Is it lies from someone out to cause trouble?'

He came towards her, each step a fresh menace, and, gripping her shoulders, he shook her mercilessly. His nostrils were flared, his mouth grim, his eyes like fires of fury. 'Well, Sapphire, I'm waiting.'

'It's not hearsay—of course not,' she protested. 'Will you let me go, you brute? You were actually seen, by a friend of mine, so there's no getting out of it.'

'And where did this *friend* supposedly see me?' He had stopped shaking her, but his fingers still bit painfully into the soft skin of her shoulders, and his eyes were savagely brilliant.

Sapphire stared back at him with equal anger. 'In London, in a hotel; on more than one occasion. Can you deny it?'

She saw by the sudden flicker in his eyes that she had touched on the truth, and her heart felt like a heavy stone within her breast. She had hoped against hope that it was all a mistake, that it had been someone else Caroline had seen. She felt sick, and as her body went limp Drake let her go.

'It's true,' he admitted, 'I was with a woman, but it's not what you think.'

'Isn't that what they all say?' flared Sapphire. 'Who was she?'

'I'm not prepared to tell you. You'll have to take my word that I wasn't having an affair.' All the fight seemed to have gone out of him. He looked ashen and drawn, and, turning away from here, he headed out into the garden.

'I'm afraid I can't do that.' Sapphire yelled after him. 'If it's a guilty conscience you're trying to hide, then you're making a very poor job of it. London's not the only——' She followed him to the door, intending to confront him with the holiday he and his mistress were supposed to have taken together, but went quiet when she saw Robin out in his garden.

For a few minutes Drake did nothing but pace up and down, completely ignoring the other man. He looked to be in the devil's own mood, his brow as black as thunder, his face taut and grim. She could not understand why he was angry. If anyone took offence it should be herself. Was it because he had been found out? Had he thought his secret safe? Was it an ongoing affair? Or had it all finished now, and that was why he was here asking her to go back to him? There was so much she did not know, and so much he was not prepared to tell.

She went back indoors, not wishing to watch his incessant pacing, intending to take the opportunity to put on some briefs and make herself less vulnerable to him, until a casual glance out of the window saw him talking to Robin. And it was no pleasant, passing-the-time-of-day conversation. The men were facing each other over the wire-link fence like two sparring tigers, and she guessed Drake had started it. She could imagine him telling Robin to keep his hands off his wife, and she hoped her neighbour was giving as good as he got. He certainly looked angry enough.

Never before had she seen Robin lose his temper. He was a sweet, gentle man, an understanding man, logical and intelligent, and yet now he was gesticulating angrily, his face turning a bright, angry red.

Sapphire watched them through narrowed, frowning eyes, wishing she could hear what was being said. At well over six feet Drake was much taller than Robin, a powerful, arrogant man, used to giving orders, used to taking charge, used to always being in the right! Nevertheless, Robin was standing up to him magnificently, his eyes never wavering from those of his opponent, and whatever it was he was saying it was having a direct effect on Drake. Her husband's fury seemed to grow with each minute, and finally he swung away in disgust and headed back towards the house.

Sapphire at once went into the attack. 'You had no right tearing into Robin like that. How dare you upset my friend?'

'*Me* upset *him*?' asked her husband harshly. 'You have it wrong there, lady. He was the one who attacked me. The man is without a doubt in love with you and is,' he went on with a snarl, 'trying to protect you from what he sees as the big bad husband.' His lip curled, baring his teeth, so that he looked for all the world like a savage animal. 'What the hell have you been telling him about me?'

Mild and gentle Robin had pitched into Drake? The very thought made Sapphire smile. She lifted her shoulders. 'I might have told him a thing or two. I was very upset yesterday; he was a great comfort to me.'

'I can imagine what kind of comfort,' Drake retorted viciously. 'I've been given a lecture for treating you badly, and I don't take kindly to that sort of thing coming from a stranger. In fact, I don't care to have our private life discussed with anyone at all.'

He towered menacingly over her, and Sapphire shivered. In all the time they had been married she had never seen this black side of him. He had lost his temper on numerous occasions, but never this badly. It was as well they had split up. There was no way she wanted this monster of a man as a husband. She looked at him with cold disdain in her eyes. 'I don't see that it matters what I told him,' she snapped, 'considering we're going to have a divorce.'

His snort of anger made her jump. 'No!' he bellowed. 'No divorce, not ever. You're coming back to me, my dear wifc, make no mistake about that.'

'You can't make me.' Her navy eyes flashed like the gemstone after which she was named.

'You think not?' A hint of a smile suddenly curved the fullness of his lips, but it was a smile without humour. 'You're forgetting, my darling, the magical power that drew us together in the first place. It has in no way diminished.'

Physical attraction, he was talking about. Yes, Drake had always excited her. He did not even have to touch her to arouse desire. Simply being close to him was sufficient. But sex was only one aspect of married life, alone it was not enough, and she had never enjoyed any of the other pleasures; there had not been enough time. Drake had never been a companion or a friend. Always he was at the beck and call of his business. The company was his whole life. It always had been and always would be. And the saddest part of all was that he didn't want children.

She must deny feeling anything. It would be foolish to go back to a man who thought this way, who not only neglected her but had no compunction about taking a mistress as well. Sapphire touched her tongue to suddenly dry lips, and it was a fatal mistake.

Drake's eyes darkened at what he took to be a provocative gesture, and before she could even anticipate his movements Sapphire found herself held firmly against him, his unyielding body pressing into her feminine softness. She felt the pounding of his heart and her own blood rushing out of control through her veins.

When his mouth swooped down on hers Sapphire knew she was lost. It happened that instantly. All rational thoughts fled beneath his onslaught, and she opened her mouth willingly to his kiss.

There was no tenderness, nothing except heat and passion and a hunger that seemed as though it would never be assuaged. It had begun hours earlier when they went to visit his grandmother, and he had said then that he intended finishing what was started. Sapphire knew she ought to put a stop to it, but already, even in these few short seconds, it was too late. The fire that licked through her veins could not be doused, and she did not want to forgo the very pleasures that she had missed so acutely during the months they were apart.

Her arms snaked up behind his head, her fingers threading through the coarseness of his hair, her body moving with unconscious rhythm against his. When, as suddenly as he had captured her, he let her go, she was stunned beyond belief.

'There's no rush, Sapphire,' he muttered. 'We have all the time in the world.'

Was this really Drake saying they had time? What had happened to the man who was always dashing here, there and everywhere, who was always too busy even for his own wife? She looked at him curiously, a faint frown drawing her fine brows together.

'You look astonished?'

'As well I might be,' she responded. 'When have you ever said that to me before?'

'Ah, but I'm on holiday now. Since I'm staying here we might as well treat it as a second honeymoon.'

If he had made the suggestion while she was still in his arms, while his mouth was against hers, while her heart was clamouring fit to burst, then she might have agreed. But now that they were standing apart, now that he had that taunting look in his eyes, she was able, vocally at least, to deny any wish to involve herself with him on that sort of level.

'You must be joking!' She hoped there was the right amount of incredulity in her voice.

'On the contrary, I'm perfectly serious. I can't guarantee the same weather as in the Bahamas, but there's no reason why we shouldn't be as happy.'

Sapphire shook her head in total disbelief. 'There's every reason. You're crazy, Drake, if you think I'd ever agree to such a preposterous suggestion.'

'We had such a wonderful time,' he said in his most persuasive voice.

Yes, thought Sapphire hollowly. They had spent most of it in bed. A wonderful time indeed. They had not been able to get enough of each other. She had really thought that their honeymoon was a taste of things to come, that the togetherness she had felt would be a permanent part of their life.

It had never occurred to her that Drake was motivated by sex alone. He worshipped her body, there was no doubt about it; he always had, and it looked as though he still did. But she wanted commitment of a different kind. There was a whole lot of things that she wanted from him that it seemed he was not prepared to give.

'And I have all the proof I need that you'll respond to me whenever I touch you. What more can a man want?' There was a satisfied smile on his face as he spoke. 'I'll go and take my much needed shower, and after that we'll discuss what we're going to do this evening.'

'Not what *we're* going to do,' she said sharply, angry with him for his assumption that he could take her whenever he liked, and angry with herself for giving away the fact that it was possible, 'what *you're* going to do. I'm going round to see Robin. I think he deserves an explanation.'

Drake's face immediately hardened and he drew in a swift, hissing breath. 'I think he's got the picture very clearly, Sapphire.'

'Your version of it,' she snapped. 'But perhaps, on second thoughts, it might be wise to wait until he's calmed down. Damn you, Drake, you're upsetting everybody with your arrogant behaviour!'

She expected another angry retort and was amazed when, with nothing more than a furious flash of his light blue eyes, he left the room.

While he was showering she changed back into her jeans and T-shirt and then washed up their cups. After that she sat down in her sitting-room and rested her head back on the chair. Drake had woken her early this morning, and so much had happened she felt absolutely worn out. The next thing she knew Drake was standing over her calling her name.

'I've cooked us a meal, Sapphire. Come on, wake up.'

She looked at him with startled blue eyes. 'How long have I been asleep?'

'A good couple of hours.' He smiled as he spoke. 'My memory hasn't faded. You looked as gorgeous asleep as you ever did. You had a secret smile on your lips as though you were having a beautiful dream. Were you?'

'I don't know,' she said with a tiny shake of her head. 'I can't remember.'

'That's a pity,' he remarked. 'I thought maybe you were dreaming about how happy we once were—and how we could be again if you'll give it another go.'

Sapphire shook her head and got up. 'That's an impossible dream, Drake. It wouldn't work, I know it wouldn't.'

'Because you don't trust me?' he asked, and his tone was surprisingly tinged with sadness.

'Because I want a husband who thinks more of his wife and home than he does his business,' she retorted wistfully.

'I guess I deserved that,' he said gruffly. 'Come and sit at the table, and we'll eat our meal before it's ruined.'

Sapphire wondered if that was the nearest thing to an apology she was ever likely to get. At least it meant he knew he had been behaving badly.

Having two meals cooked for her in one day was a rare treat for Sapphire. In fact, it was the first time Drake had ever done it, and she was surprised at how good the spaghetti bolognese was. He had opened a bottle of red wine as well and put flowers on the table, and he was at his most charming throughout the entire meal.

'It's a pity you changed back into your jeans,' he said at one point, but then he changed to a different topic of conversation and the awkwardness passed.

He was once again the charming, flirtatious companion who had wooed her in the early days of their relationship, and Sapphire found herself laughing and talking and relating anecdotes, often leaning towards him with something more than innocent amusement in her eyes.

He frequently refilled her glass, and she felt bubbly and happy and without a care in the world. She hadn't enjoyed an evening so much in a long time. They sat at the table for hours, long after it had grown dark, and Drake had lit a candle, albeit an ordinary white household one, but it still had the effect of adding a magical air to the occasion.

To her pleasure and surprise he did not mention work once. In the past he had always talked business, and it was a pleasant change to be able to discuss other things. All in all, it was like getting to know each other all over again.

Sapphire felt happier than she had in a long time, until the clock struck midnight and Drake pushed back his chair. 'I think it's time we went to bed.' And she could tell by the satisfied smile on his face that he meant the two of them together.

CHAPTER SIX

SAPPHIRE looked at Drake sharply. 'Wasn't that a slip of the tongue? *We* are not doing anything. *I* am going to bed by myself. Thank you for this evening—it's been lovely, unexpectedly so.' She might have drunk more wine than she was used to, but she was still in full control of her faculties and there was no way Drake was joining her in bed.

His mouth twisted into a rueful smile. 'You sound determined.'

'I am, I assure you,' she said firmly.

'Then I can do no more than say goodnight, my lovely wife.' His hands cupped her face as his lips brushed hers so briefly she could almost have imagined it. But her response wasn't imagined. Senses ignited and pulses raced, and she did not want to go upstairs by herself. She wanted him in bed with her, there was no doubt about it, but she dared not give in to her feelings. Making love wouldn't solve the real issue.

'Goodnight,' she whispered, their eyes meeting and holding for several heart-stopping seconds; but he did not detain her. It was not until she got to the top of the stairs that he called her name. She turned and looked down, and her heart leapt yet again.

'Have you any spare sheets?'

The question was something of an anticlimax, not at all what she had expected, and surprise registered on her face. 'There's a quilt in the airing cupboard—I'll get it for you.'

'No need.' Drake took the stairs two at a time. 'I'll reach it out myself.' Within seconds he was at her side, and Sapphire had to exert every ounce of self-control not to fling herself into his arms, and when he lightly kissed her again before going downstairs it was almost her undoing.

Before she had even started to undress he tapped on her bedroom door, and she opened it with a touch of impatience on her face. If he was trying to wear her down he was going the right way about it. 'What now?' she asked, deliberately making her tone sharp.

'I need a pillow.'

She walked over to her own bed and snatched one up. 'Here you are.'

'I couldn't deprive you.' He walked into her room but did not take it from her.

'It's all right—I usually throw one off the bed anyway.'

'If you're sure?'

'Yes, I'm sure,' she said firmly. 'Come on, Drake, play the game. I know exactly what you're doing, but I'm not going to change my mind. Everything has to be right between us before I sleep with you again.'

For a second she thought he was going to debate the point, then with a slow shrug, and a long lingering look that set the whole of her body tingling, he turned and left the room. It took all Sapphire's will-power not to call him back, his name actually forming on her lips, but the door closed and she heard his footsteps going downstairs, and she let out her breath on a sigh of relief.

She whipped off her jeans and top and pulled on her nightdress, then scuttled out to the bathroom, making it back again to the seclusion of her room before she heard Drake come up the stairs again and go into the bathroom himself. She could see it was going to be difficult maintaining strict privacy. It would become a cat-

and-mouse game if Drake stayed in the cottage for any length of time.

Sleep proved impossible. She was far too conscious of her husband downstairs, and the fact that she had already had a couple of hours' sleep made a difference as well. She wondered whether Drake was having the same problem; whether he was thinking of her up here. She was afraid to open her door and listen in case he heard and took it as an invitation.

At some stage or other she must have dropped off, because a loud noise awoke her—a tremendous bang that made her sit bolt upright in bed, her heart pounding. Then a flash of lightning lit the sky and she heard rain lashing against her window.

Another roll of thunder overhead and an immediate streak of silver made her shoot back beneath the quilt and pull it firmly over her head. She put her hands over her ears in a vain endeavour to shut out the hateful sounds—then nearly jumped out of her skin when something touched her on the shoulder.

'I'm here, Sapphire, there's no need to be afraid.' The cover was gently pulled back and Drake's strong arms gathered her against the reassuring warmth of his chest. He held her head against him, one hand over her eyes to block out the flashes of lightning, the other stroking her hair, all the time murmuring words of comfort.

This was only the second occasion he had ever consoled her, even though he knew her fear of storms. Every other time he had been away on business and she had been left to suffer on her own. Another peal of thunder had her burying herself into his chest, her hands clapped again over her ears, her whole body trembling with fear.

'It's all right, my darling, it's all right.' His voice and hands soothed. 'I'm here to look after you. Nothing's going to hurt, I promise.' He lifted his legs on to the bed and lay alongside her, and it seemed like hours to Sapphire before the storm faded into the distance, and even when the thunder could no longer be heard Drake still held her in his arms. In all truthfulness Sapphire did not want him to let her go; she wanted him to spend the rest of the night in her bed.

She awoke with a smile on her face. She had been dreaming, dreaming that she and Drake were back together and everything was perfect. He no longer worked long hours, and life had taken on a honeymoon-like quality. Their love life was, if possible, better than ever, and at long last he had said he would like a child.

When she opened her eyes she felt as though she were floating on a cloud, happier than she had been at any time since meeting Drake—and then she remembered. It was nothing like that at all. Although he wanted her back she could not accept that things would be any different.

Her thoughts then fled to last night when he had come to her bed, when she had wanted him to stay with her, had wanted it so badly that she had almost begged him not to go, and had been disappointed beyond measure when the storm finally ended and after reassuring himself that she was all right he had put her from him and left the room.

In one respect she was grateful he hadn't taken advantage, because there would have been no going back once their physical relationship was resumed; in another she was frustrated. She had been so aroused, so desirous of him—even her dream had added to the feelings that surged and tumbled inside her.

She was almost afraid to face him this morning in case he saw her burning thoughts. He knew her far too well for her to keep her feelings hidden. Perhaps this was his plan—to get her more and more excited and more and more frustrated until in the end she would willingly fall into his arms and agree to go back to Treetops.

A glance at the clock told her that it was just after eight, and when she finally went downstairs it was to find Drake missing, although his car was still outside. He had either gone for a walk to while away the minutes until she got up, or to the village shop for a newspaper, although she could have told him they didn't sell them except on a Sunday.

He had always been an early riser, getting up about six each morning and spending an hour or two in his study before going to work. The kettle was still hot, so she switched it on and made herself a cup of tea, then wandered into the back garden to drink it.

The birds were in full voice this sunny morning, and she paused a moment looking up at the sturdy horse-chestnut tree, turning with a smile when she heard her name spoken.

'Robin!' She welcomed the opportunity to speak to him. 'I didn't see you there.'

'Your husband stayed the night.'

It was reproach rather than a question, and Sapphire nodded and gave a rueful grimace at the same time. 'I didn't want him to, Robin, but when Drake makes up his mind there's no stopping him.'

'He wants to repair your marriage?'

She nodded.

'How do you feel about it?'

She sighed and was so long in answering that Robin did it for her.

'You still love him, don't you?'

'I'm not sure,' said Sapphire. 'I feel something for him, yes, but I don't know whether it's love, and I certainly don't want to go back to him, not under the same conditions as we had before.'

'And do you think there's any chance of him changing?'

'No, I don't,' she said with a vigorous shake of her head. 'Oh, he said he would, but I don't know whether I can believe him. We have a lot of talking to do before I reach a decision.'

'Did he sleep with you last night?'

Sapphire was shocked by such an intimate question, and looked at her neighbour in surprise.

'I'm sorry,' he said quickly. 'I shouldn't have asked, but—well, the truth of the matter is that I'm jealous. You do know that I love you, Sapphire?'

She gave a faint nod. 'I guessed as much, and I'm sorry, Robin—I've never felt anything for you other than friendship. I thought you knew that.'

'I do,' he answered regretfully. 'It was all wishful thinking on my part. I don't want you to be unhappy, though. Don't do anything you might later regret, Sapphire, and remember, I'm always here if you need a shoulder to cry on.'

He was so good and kind that Sapphire wished she did love him; she hated hurting him. 'Thank you, Robin.' She leaned over the fence and touched her lips to his cheek. 'You're a friend in a million.'

'Where did you go yesterday?'

'To see Drake's grandmother.' Sapphire knew he was thinking that he should have been with her, that Drake turning up unexpectedly had upset all their plans. In the light of his confession she wondered now whether it would have been a wise move going to London. Perhaps Robin had thought that with a change of environment she might think differently about him? She had half guessed that he felt more for her than she did him, but he had always been too much of a gentleman to do or say anything about it. He had always recognised that she was not ready for another relationship. She surmised that now he thought it was too late.

'His grandmother?' asked Robin in surprise. 'That sounds as though he's serious about you getting back together.'

'Deadly serious,' came Drake's gruff voice over her shoulder. His arm curved about Sapphire's waist and his lips nuzzled her neck.

Neither of them had seen her husband approach, and Sapphire instinctively tried to jerk away, but his arm tightened and his smile widened, though she knew there was no sincerity behind it. He was angry, extremely so, and it triggered a similar fury that he should object to her speaking to Robin.

'How dare you listen to our conversation?' she snapped through gritted teeth. 'You have no right creeping up and eavesdropping like that!'

'I think I have every right, when you were talking about me.' Drake's eyes shot to Robin, dark and dangerous. 'I don't like our affairs being discussed with a stranger. Perhaps I didn't make it clear enough yesterday that Sapphire is most definitely returning home? If you're trying to persuade her otherwise then you're wasting your time. Keep your hands off her, my man—Sapphire belongs to me.'

'How dare you?' spat Sapphire before her astonished neighbour could say a word. 'Robin is my friend. I'll talk to him whenever I feel like it, about any subject. He's been very good to me, and if you think that because you've turned up I'm going to ignore him then you can think again!'

'I'm not trying to come between you and your wife,' put in Robin anxiously, 'though surely you can understand that we've grown reasonably close during the time Sapphire's been my neighbour. It's inevitable.'

'Too close for my liking,' snarled Drake.

Robin shook his head, as though finding it difficult to believe this man was attacking him so viciously. 'Considering you were separated, and as far as I knew there was no chance of you getting back together, then I saw no reason why we shouldn't be friends.'

'You're old enough to be her damn father,' growled Drake. 'It's positively indecent!'

'Now hold on!' grated Robin. 'Sapphire's twenty-three and I'm sixteen years older—not the sort of age difference you're talking about. My own daughter is seventeen—now if I were chasing seventeen-year-olds then you'd be within your rights to say something, but Sapphire is as much a woman as I'm a man, and I—— '

'So you are admitting that there's something going on between you?' cut in Drake harshly.

'I'm admitting nothing,' retorted Robin. 'But the way you treated your wife, I'm not surprised she walked out on you.'

'Why, you——'

'Drake, please.' Sapphire took hold of his arm as he lunged across the fence. 'This is crazy. Please, let's go back inside and talk this thing over rationally.'

Drake shook her off. 'How can I be rational, with that creep ogling you all the time? My God, who knows what's been going on?'

'Since you let her walk out of your life it's none of your business,' fired Robin, a flush of high colour deepening his cheeks, his brown eyes flashing furiously.

Sapphire knew she had to part the two men before the whole scene turned more ugly than it already was. 'You'd better go in, Robin,' she said quietly. If she couldn't get Drake to walk away then this was the only alternative.

'Not until your husband apologises.'

A feeling of impending disaster washed over Sapphire, and she turned her attention back to Drake. 'Please, Drake, you're being ridiculous. If I can't talk to my neighbour then it's a sad world. If it were a woman living next door you wouldn't think twice about it. You really are being too sensitive. Robin is a friend, that's all; we've done nothing to make you jealous. Stop this arguing, for goodness' sake.'

Drake looked at her and the fierce anger in his eyes made her stomach tighten, but she smiled bravely and whispered, 'Please.'

He glared again at Robin, then with a shrug turned and marched back into the house. Sapphire gave her neighbour an apologetic smile and followed.

For a few seconds silence reigned. Drake seemed to be chewing the situation over in his mind, and when he turned to her some of his anger had faded. Nevertheless he still looked far from happy about the situation. 'I think the sooner I get you back home the better,' he said.

'You make me sound like a runaway child!' Sapphire protested. 'I'm an adult, I'm my own person, you can't take me back if I don't want to come.'

'Last night I could have made love to you.' There was a narrowed, glittering intensity to his eyes and they never once left her face.

Last night she could have let him, but not now, not with him treating her as though she were some possession to be picked up and carried about whenever he wished, not when he angered and threatened her neighbour and made erroneous assumptions. Heaven knew what motivated him; he had acted like a jealous man, but this was something she had already dismissed. To be jealous you had to be in love, and Drake was definitely not in love with her. It was doubtful he ever had been. He desired her, yes, but love, real love, was something he was not capable of.

'How I felt last night has nothing to do with it,' she retorted. 'I left you because I wasn't happy with our marriage. I can't see things being any different. Your attitude towards me leaves very much to be desired. It's obvious you don't trust me, you don't believe a word I say about Robin—what sort of a basis is that for a reconciliation?'

'You don't like it when the boot's on the other foot, do you?' he snarled. 'You didn't accept my explanation about the woman I was with in London, but I'm expected to accept yours, even though you give the impression that you've been living in each other's pockets. Really, Sapphire, saying I don't trust you is no reason at all. I'm not an idiot, you know—I have eyes, I can see what's going on. But regardless, you still feel something for me.'

'More's the pity,' she snapped. 'It's me who's the idiot for not being able to get you out of my system. But I'm older and wiser than I used to be. I no longer let my heart rule my head. I'm better off without you, Drake, and let's face it, you're better off without me.'

His eyes still bored into hers. 'That's a matter of opinion. I wouldn't be here now if I didn't want you back, and the sooner you accept that the better.'

' "Let battle commence",' said Sapphire bitterly.

His eyes narrowed. 'I thrive on challenges, dear wife of mine.'

She wished he wouldn't keep calling her his wife. As far as she was concerned she had given up that title, and the fault was his. He was just too stubborn to admit it.

Breakfast was a silent meal, each eyeing the other but saying nothing. Sapphire had a busy day in front of her.

The owners of a large private house in Zennor had agreed to her photographing their prized, rare species of orchids. It had taken her a long time to set up, and she was definitely not going to let Drake spoil her plans.

Almost as though he knew what she was thinking he said abruptly, 'If you have any plans for today forget them. We're going to sit here and have a long-overdue talk.'

'Oh, no, we're not,' Sapphire retorted at once. 'You can't come here and expect to take over my life. I can't neglect my photography just because you've turned up. I'm going out.'

'Surely taking a few snapshots isn't that important?'

The derogatory tone of his voice lifted her hackles. 'You have no idea how important my work is to me. I'm sorry, Drake, but I have an appointment that I have no intention of cancelling.'

'Then I'll come with you,' he said firmly.

But Sapphire did not want Drake accompanying her. It would be impossible to concentrate on such precise photography with him at her side. She shook her head. 'I don't think so—I work better alone.'

'You don't even let your *friend* go with you?'

She flashed him a disparaging glance. 'Never.'

'And does it take you far afield, this work of yours?'

'Here and there. Not far enough to have to stay out overnight; I make sure of that.'

A frown drew his brows together as her barb struck home. 'It's an entirely different field that I work in. It's inevitable that I spend time away from home.'

'It's not inevitable at all,' she snapped. 'You're just too obsessed with what you do. You never trust anyone else to do the job as well as you.'

'It seems to me that we've had this conversation before,' he muttered.

'And it made not a scrap of difference,' Sapphire returned sharply. 'Excuse me, I have to get ready.' She pushed her chair back from the table and stood up; Drake did the same. But while she went upstairs he cleared the table and washed the dishes. This new, domesticated side of him continued to amaze her.

When she went back downstairs armed with her bulging camera bag Drake looked at her and frowned. 'You carry that around with you all the time?'

She nodded. 'Of course. What did you think, I'd just take a camera over my shoulder and that was it? It's obvious you know nothing about photography.'

'I didn't realise you were so serious.'

Sapphire lifted her shoulders. 'So now you do. I'll see you when I get back, if you're still here.'

'I will be,' Drake announced firmly. 'Will you be long?' He looked as though he would still like to come with her.

'I've no idea,' she said. 'Expect me when you see me.' It would do him good to have a taste of his own medicine.

Her actual photo session did not take as long as she had imagined. Conditions in the hothouses were perfect, no breeze to disturb the delicate petals as so often happened out of doors, when she could spend ages carefully making a windbreak out of pieces of card or ramming a piece of wire into the ground and tying individual flowers to it. Here there were no such problems.

But instead of going back home she drove to one of her favourite little bays and spent an hour or two photographing harbour life. It was something she did occasionally for her own pleasure. She was actually building up quite a library of pictures of different seaside villages and thought that perhaps one day she might turn them into a book. They were not the usual scenes one saw in travel guides, but pictures of people and everyday objects seen from a different viewpoint. She found it quite challenging, and spent more time there than she intended.

It was four in the afternoon when she got home, to discover a strange car parked outside the cottage. Sapphire frowned faintly, wondering who it belonged to. Indoors all was quiet and empty, no sign of Drake or anyone else. It was not until she looked through the sitting-room window that she saw her visitor was no other than her friend Caroline.

She broke into an instinctive smile—until she saw the way her friend was looking at Drake. Her husband sat with his back to her, so she could not see his expression, but Caroline was flirting like mad, never once taking her eyes off his face, her lips parted suggestively, her body gravitating towards his, and even as Sapphire watched she touched his arm, stroking in an intimate way that suggested it was not the first time they had been together.

Caroline and Drake! It was an alarming thought, though now she came to think about it her friend had visited Treetops quite frequently when Drake was at home, and often she had been on her own with him while Sapphire was making a drink or a sandwich. Sapphire had never thought anything about it because Caroline had come at other times as well, but now she began to wonder.

It was Caroline who had told her she had seen Drake in London with another woman. Had she known it was entirely innocent? Had she deliberately turned the knife in an already painful wound? Had she wanted them to split up? Did she have her eye on him herself? Was she the other woman, in fact? By walking out had Sapphire left her a clear field? It was strange that Caroline had turned up now when she had not once put in an appearance during the last six months. She had telephoned, yes, but that was all.

Was it really possible that there was something going on between her husband and this attractive blonde? Had something gone wrong with their relationship? Was that why Drake had turned up here, because he had finished with Caroline? Had Caroline come running after him to try and patch things up? A thousand and one questions raced through Sapphire's mind as she stood there and watched them, watched Caroline lean forward and touch her lips to Drake's. And he made no attempt to stop her!

With a sharp cry of pain Sapphire moved away from the window, pausing a moment to calm herself before joining them, making sure her footsteps were heard before she was in sight.

'Caroline!' She made herself sound joyful. 'What a surprise. You're the last person I expected to see.' As she had envisaged, her friend was sitting demurely in her garden chair, and there was nothing at all in her demeanour or expression to suggest that a few seconds earlier she had been making up to Drake.

'Sapphire—I come all this way to see you and you're not in.' Caroline sprang to her feet and even managed to inject a note of reproach into her voice.

'You should have phoned and told me you were coming,' Sapphire told her. 'I hope Drake's been looking after you?'

'Indeed he has.' Caroline gave Drake a smile as he too got up and pulled out another chair for Sapphire to join them, but there was none of the intimacy Sapphire had observed earlier, it was the smile of a casual acquaintance.

She searched Drake's face as well, but there was nothing to suggest that the blonde girl meant anything to him. Perhaps she had imagined things? Caroline was a very warm, friendly person, a bit of a flirt, always popular with the men at the photographic society. Was she reading more into the situation than there really was? Was she looking for something that wasn't there?

'Drake tells me you've been out burning a few frames?'

'More than a few,' agreed Sapphire, dropping on to her seat, thinking of the several rolls of film she had exposed and was itching to develop.

'I hear you're making quite a name for yourself these days.'

Sapphire lifted her shoulders in a modest shrug. 'I'm doing all right.'

'Doing all right? Hark at her!' said Caroline with a laughing glance at Drake. 'Nearly every gardening magazine you look at these days, and a few others besides, has a photograph in it somewhere by Sapphire Rivelin. She's incredible. I never suspected when I asked her to join the photographic society that she had such talent.'

'Nor did I,' smiled Sapphire. 'And if Drake hadn't bought me my first camera I might never have discovered it.'

'So it's all thanks to you that we have such a talented person in our midst?' Caroline's green eyes rested on Drake and he smiled back at her, and this time Sapphire was sure she saw something more than just friendship. Unexpected jealousy rose and threatened to choke her, and she looked away quickly, not wanting to see the flame that burned between the two of them.

'Are you all right?' Drake observed the sudden pallor of her cheeks.

Sapphire swallowed hard and nodded. 'I could do with a drink.' It suddenly occurred to her that she had neither eaten nor drunk anything since breakfast.

Instantly Drake sprang to his feet and went into the house. Caroline watched him go, and then as if realising she could be giving herself away she turned back to

Sapphire with a smile. 'I hadn't realised your husband was here.' A barefaced lie if ever there was one, thought Sapphire bitterly. 'You can imagine my surprise when I came expecting to see you and he opened the door. Have you resolved your differences? Are you getting back together?'

It seemed like a perfectly innocent question, but Sapphire saw her friend's underlying anxiety and she jutted her chin. 'It's early days, but I think there's every possibility.'

There was the briefest flicker in Caroline's eyes to show that her words were a disappointment. 'Is that why he's here, to patch things up?'

Sapphire nodded. 'I don't mind telling you it was quite a shock when he turned up, but I'm glad he came, because we needed to talk.' Not for anything would she give away the fact that all the talking they had done so far had led nowhere.

At that moment Drake returned with glasses of lemonade and a plate of biscuits, and conversation turned general. Caroline's eyes were frequently on Drake, though to give him his due he gave absolutely nothing away. If she hadn't seen them together earlier Sapphire would never have suspected them.

It was not until she was getting ready to leave that Caroline said, 'Oh, by the way, my sister's thinking of selling this cottage. She's getting married and doesn't really need the income any longer. It won't be for a while, but I thought I should warn you that you might have to get out.'

Sapphire felt disappointment shudder through her nerve-streams and wished Caroline had told her when they were on their own. Now Drake knew he would use the information to persuade her to go back with him.

Already there was a gleam in his eye and a secret smile curving his lips.

There was a solution, though—she could buy the cottage herself; she could afford it now. Yes, it was something definitely worth looking into. She would get in touch with Lorna Brecon and find out how much she was asking.

Drake walked Caroline out to her car, and as she sat behind the wheel he leaned towards her to say his goodbye. Considering Caroline was supposed to be *her* friend, thought Sapphire, they were being particularly indiscreet.

'I'll come and see you again, if you don't mind,' said Caroline to Sapphire over Drake's shoulder. 'I've enjoyed today very much.'

'Shouldn't you have been at work?' asked Sapphire.

Caroline smiled. 'I'm on my holidays. I was going to America but changed my mind, and now I'm at a loose end.'

'I'm not in very often,' admitted Sapphire. 'My photography takes me out quite a lot. You'd better ring next time.'

'Oh, I don't mind your—er—husband entertaining me,' said Caroline.

'Drake isn't staying long,' Sapphire snapped.

'Is that true?' Caroline looked up at Drake with her wide green eyes. 'Are you coming back home?'

'Shortly,' he said. 'Like you, I'm taking a few days' holiday.'

'And Sapphire's working? Poor you.'

'I have assignments fixed up that I can't get out of, but it doesn't mean to say we shan't be spending quite a lot of time together,' said Sapphire firmly, wishing the girl would hurry up and go.

Drake touched Caroline's arm. 'Have a safe journey.'

She gave him a brilliant smile as she started the engine, and he stood and watched until she was out of sight. Sapphire did not need any more proof.

CHAPTER SEVEN

'YOU weren't very friendly to Caroline,' said Drake, once they were indoors.

'You more than made up,' Sapphire snapped, running hot water into the washing up bowl.

'And what's that supposed to mean?' There was a sudden tension in him that, as far as Sapphire was concerned, was a further sign of guilt.

'It means that you two looked pretty close when I came home.'

He shook his head. 'What are you talking about? I was simply entertaining your friend.'

'*Entertaining* being the operative word?' she flashed back. She squeezed liquid into the water and swished it around before starting to wash the glasses they had used earlier. She was glad she had her back to Drake. She did not want to see any sign on his face of his infatuation for Caroline.

'You're jealous?' There was a mixture of incredulity and delight in his voice. 'You think that Caroline and I——' He broke off and laughed. 'This is really rich. Why would I want to involve myself with a girl like Caroline when I have you?'

'But that's just it,' returned Sapphire sharply. 'You don't *have* me. I—ouch!'

'What have you done?' Drake was instantly behind her.

'Cut myself.' She had been washing up with such vehemence that she had broken a glass, and now blood oozed from her finger with no sign of stopping.

Drake immediately handed her a piece of kitchen paper. 'Here, press this on to it while I get the first-aid box. I saw one in the bathroom, didn't I?'

Sapphire nodded.

Within seconds he was back, drying and cleaning the cut, which was quite deep. He was gentle and concerned, and Sapphire felt a resurrection of feelings she kept desperately trying to stem. Despite Caroline, despite everything, he still had this power over her. It seemed as though, whatever happened, however he treated her, it would never go away.

'Caroline doesn't mean a thing to me,' he said softly as he worked.

'That wasn't what it looked like,' murmured Sapphire. 'I saw you through the window before I came out into the garden.'

'Caroline's a flirt,' he admitted.

'Well, yes, I know that, but——'

'You saw something that wasn't there. Caroline's not my type.'

He was trying to get out of it, she thought, saying all these things to take her mind away from the truth. She knew what she had seen—and when Caroline kissed him he hadn't shrugged it off as he would have done if he hadn't been interested. He was lying, but she did not want to make an issue of it, so she shrugged, and as soon as he had fixed a piece of sticking-plaster on her finger she moved away.

'I'll finish the washing up,' he said. 'Go and sit outside and enjoy the last of the sun.'

It sounded like a good idea to her. The more distance she put between them the better. She wondered if he had any idea what he had done to her by standing so close. Any idea that her heartbeats had quickened or a warmth suffused her body that had nothing at all to do with the heat of the day.

She was aware that he could see her through the kitchen window, and it did nothing to ease the tumult inside her, and when he came out and joined her it was like a steamroller going over her chest. If only she could be immune to him, if only he would go away—for ever.

'It looks as though I'm having my job done for me,' Drake observed.

'What do you mean?' Sapphire frowned as she looked up at him.

'You're going to lose your lodgings after all.' There was pleasure in his eyes and his lips curled in happy anticipation of her moving back in with him.

Sapphire's glare was one of anger. 'I wouldn't be too sure of that if I were you.'

A faint frown lodged on his brow. 'You have other plans?'

'Not yet,' she answered easily. 'But I have an idea which I think will work out very well.'

He glanced at her sharply. 'I want you to come back home, Sapphire. Your place is with me.'

She drew in a deep, unsteady breath. 'When are you going to accept, Drake, that it's all over between us? That I no longer want to be your wife, that the sooner we get a divorce the better?'

'Never,' he told her curtly. 'And I don't think you mean it either. Your feelings for me aren't dead—I'd be an idiot if I thought that. You've already shown me how much you still care, and your jealousy over Caroline is yet more proof. I don't know what you're trying to prove by keeping your distance, but there'll come a day when you can hold out no longer. I'm not going to give up. Perhaps you've never realised before what a persistent person I can be.'

'I've never had time to find out very much about you,' she snapped. 'You were what I'd call an absentee husband. It wasn't like being married at all.'

A muscle jerked in his jaw. 'I'm not going to be allowed to forget that, am I?'

'You bet not,' she tossed back. 'It's what finished our marriage. The truth of the matter is, Drake, that you're not good husband material. You should never have married. You're not the type to settle down. Oh, maybe in ten years' time, but not yet—you're still too full of plans and enthusiasm for your business.'

'I don't think that's a bad thing,' he said harshly.

'Not if you're more interested in making money than keeping your wife happy.'

His eyes narrowed dangerously. 'You'd have been content to live in poverty?'

'Not exactly,' she confessed, 'but——'

'Not exactly,' he repeated savagely. 'Marrying a rich man was more than just a childish dream, wasn't it, Sapphire? I remember you saying when we first met that money was important to you, so I should have been forewarned. You even had the gall to accuse me of working too hard and neglecting you. What was it you wanted, woman, the best of both worlds?'

'How dare you?' she spat savagely. 'You're a mile off the mark. I married you because I loved you, for no other reason.'

His eyes narrowed. 'So why did you turn up when I stopped your allowance?'

'It was coincidence!' she cried, shaking her hands furiously in the air, hating the thought that he was still accusing her of being a gold-digger. She hadn't even realised that he had stopped her allowance. 'Why would I have left you if I'd wanted your money?' she demanded angrily. 'If that's really all I was interested in it wouldn't have mattered to me that you were out at work all the hours God made.'

'So you tell me where the money's gone,' he thrust back with equal fury. 'I've checked with the bank manager, and most of what I put into your account is missing.'

Sapphire glared. 'Are you saying it wasn't mine to spend?'

He shook his head. 'Of course not—I just want the truth. You enjoy spending money, that's it, isn't it?' His fingers curled and uncurled at his sides, making it look as though he would like to shake the truth out of her.

How little he knew her. She had never spent his money as though there were no tomorrow, and if her mother hadn't been ill she wouldn't have touched a penny of it now. Admittedly, it had been nice to have money in her pocket to spend on herself alone, but she had never been reckless. Her upbringing had seen to that. Most of her clothes and jewellery had been bought by Drake himself.

Her eyes were savage as she faced him. 'I don't have to tell you what I've done with it.' If he thought so badly of her what purpose would be served by telling him the truth? If he loved her he would trust her, he wouldn't be asking all these questions. It was yet another black mark against him.

'Then I can only assume that you're guilty, and that it was money you came begging for.'

Sapphire drew in a deep, unsteady breath. 'There are times when I hate you, Drake Rivelin!'

'And others when you love me,' he returned, a cynical smile deepening the grooves at the side of his mouth.

'That died a long time ago,' Sapphire claimed fiercely, pushing herself to her feet. 'Excuse me, I've had enough of this conversation.'

Next time she saw Louise she would definitely give her a piece of her mind. Her sister had no right telling Drake such rubbish. She must have known it was nothing more than a childish dream. Or was it? Sapphire went up to her room and threw herself down on the bed. When she had met Drake he had been everything she had ever wanted in a man—handsome, wealthy, intelligent, successful. Had she fallen in love with what he was instead of who he was?

She had had plenty of dates with boys her own age, and none of them had done a thing for her, even if they'd been good-looking. The fact was that none of them had had enough money to impress her. They'd always spent their week's wage packet before the next one was due. No one had ever lavished her with flowers, like Drake had, no one had bought her expensive presents, no one had taken her to classy restaurants.

She hated to think he could be right, that she had fallen in love with the image instead of reality. All of a sudden she felt tears prick the backs of her eyelids. What if it were true? What if she had never truly loved Drake, the man? But if it were, why would she have been upset when he was away so often? Because she had no one to take her out? He still bought her presents, he always telephoned; shouldn't that have been enough? He had only neglected her because he was making money to spend on her. Wasn't that a form of love in itself? Had she been wrong to doubt him? But how about his infidelity? insisted a tiny voice. Wasn't that the real breaking point?

Her whole body felt weary and she let the tears fall without making any attempt to stop them. All of a sudden she was totally confused. She had always thought she knew what was right and what was wrong, and what her feelings were and what Drake's feelings were; now she wasn't sure any more.

It was a long time before she went back downstairs, and when she did Drake had gone out. His car was missing and she thought he might have left and gone home, until she checked and found his clothes were still there.

Maybe he was giving her time to herself? Maybe he felt he had given her food for thought and she should be left alone to digest it? Maybe he had plenty to think about too? She had done more thinking in this last hour than she had in all the months since they had split up.

She made herself a cup of tea and wondered what the next step should be. Buy this house and live a lonely existence without Drake? Or go back to him and see what they could rescue of their marriage? Would it work? Or would it be as bad or even worse than before? How would she know unless she tried it?

She decided to telephone Lorna and find out exactly what the situation was with the cottage, tell her she might be interested in buying it herself, but with the receiver in her hand and half the numbers dialled she put it down again. Was this really what she wanted? The answer had to be no; she wanted to go back to Drake, but she also wanted an assurance that he would be at home most evenings and that he would be completely faithful to her. She would not mind the odd night away, but she could not stomach him being absent for weeks on end. And there was the question of children. Would he agree to starting a family? This was an issue she had yet to discuss with him, although she thought she knew what his answer would be. He had been very adamant on that point.

It suddenly occurred to her that she was starving, and as she knew there was nothing much in the fridge she decided to go down to the inn which was no more than a hundred yards away. According to Robin the Punch Bowl had a varied history. In more than four hundred years it had been used as a courthouse, a coaching inn and a smugglers' distribution centre. It was also interesting in that it had no bar. Robin had told Sapphire that it was one of the last inns in Britain which preferred to use the old-fashioned term, 'kitchen' a room which had wooden tables and benches and a flagged stone floor.

To begin with she had the long restaurant to herself, but soon it began to fill up with holidaymakers and the sound of endless conversations filled the air. When she looked down the length of the room and saw Drake sitting at the same table as an attractive brunette, wild jealousy rose up in her throat. As though he felt her eyes on him he glanced across, smiling when he saw her, and after a few muttered words to his companion he pushed back his chair and came to join her.

Heads turned as he walked down the room; taller than most people present, unconsciously arrogant and lethally attractive. Even in his casual white shirt and trousers he easily stood out from the rest of the holidaymakers, and as he approached Sapphire's table several envious glances were sent in her direction.

'Who was that?' she asked sharply.

At the same time he said, 'What are you doing here?'

'I'm having a meal, what does it look as if I'm doing?' she hissed tetchily.

'Do you eat here often?' he asked with a frown, drawing out the chair opposite and sitting.

'Only if I have no food in the house,' she retorted. 'Why are *you* here? Who is that woman?'

He shrugged and spread his hands expansively. 'I've no idea. We shared a table because there were no others.'

'You looked mighty friendly.'

'Your green eye's showing.' He wagged a warning finger. 'You're getting paranoid about the opposite sex.'

With just cause, Sapphire muttered beneath her breath. Aloud she said, 'I didn't expect you back yet.'

'Were you hoping I'd gone altogether?'

'The thought did cross my mind.'

'I'm sorry to disappoint you.'

He beckoned a waitress and told her he had changed tables, and the meal he had ordered was duly brought to him. As Sapphire was well into her main course by this time she could see them sitting here for a long while yet.

All in all the evening was much pleasanter than Sapphire had anticipated. Drake put himself out to be excellent company, keeping her amused and interested all the time. They went for a walk through the lanes afterwards, with his arm about her shoulders, and once or twice he brushed his lips against her cheek, and when they got back to the cottage Sapphire was glowing with happiness.

It was like falling in love all over again. He was treating her with deference and respect as if they had just met. He wasn't asking anything of her that she was not prepared to give, and because of that she was actually warming towards him. It was unbelievable, but she was.

When they got indoors he suggested a drink of chocolate before they went to bed. Again Sapphire was astounded. She had never known Drake drink chocolate before; at home whisky was his usual nightcap. He put on the kettle and made the drinks while she wandered out into the garden.

It was one of those rare balmy evenings, the sky star-spangled, the odd night bird calling, the scent of stock—which she had planted deliberately for its perfume—

lingering in the still air. They should be drinking champagne, she thought, or at the very least a good wine.

She found it incongruous to be clutching a hot, steaming mug when the whole scene was so evocative. Drake stood close to her, so close she could feel the warmth of him. But more than that she sensed that the evening meant something to him too. He was as aware of her as she was of him—and yet he did nothing about it!

This surprised her. The Drake she knew had never lost any opportunity to satisfy his desire. By now she would have been held in his arms, pulled against that powerful, exciting body, his mouth drinking from hers, draining her, arousing her.

The physical side of their relationship had been a constant source of pleasure. She had fed on it, thrived on it, needed it—as she needed him now! She moved away from him, pretending to be looking at the garden. The light from the kitchen window spilled down the path and she could see everything clearly.

There was no light on in Robin's house, and she wondered whether he had gone to bed, or whether he was watching them from a darkened window. She felt sorry for him, because not only was he suffering from unrequited love, he was also the butt of Drake's anger. And he had asked for none of it; all he had done was befriend her, for which she would be eternally grateful.

Drake came up to her and turned her to face him. He had finished his drink and put down his mug, and now he took her face between his palms and kissed her. It was a gentle kiss, a careful kiss, nevertheless it sent sensations surging through each and every one of her limbs. 'This is one thing that's never changed, Sapphire,' he muttered.

But before she could respond, before she could give in to the aching sensations that had been with her all evening, he had freed her again.

'Don't you agree?'

Sapphire did not answer. It was a crazy situation. She wanted him so much, but knew she must not show it, and Drake—well, he clearly wanted her as well and yet was playing some sort of waiting game. He knew what he was doing, she felt sure, and the fact that she knew as well did not make it any easier. In effect it was like some form of long, slow torture, the pain increasing gradually, the knowledge of what the outcome was going to be adding to the agony.

'You haven't answered my question, Sapphire.' Then after a pause, when she still said nothing, he went on, 'Maybe I wasn't such a good husband; nevertheless I know more about you than you imagine. I know everything you feel and desire, every little sensation that trickles its way through your beautiful body, every tiny response, almost every thought.'

Sapphire believed him. He had always, on the occasions they were together, paid her a great deal of attention, made her the hub of his universe. Their honeymoon had been absolutely magical, there wasn't a second when they weren't intent on each other, but it had all faded once they came home and his work took over. They'd had weekends and some evenings to begin with, but even they had got less and less frequent, until in the end she had wondered what type of a man it was she had married. She couldn't live for ever on memories of an exciting two weeks in the Bahamas.

'If you know so much then you should also know that our marriage is over.' She spoke softly, almost regretfully, no censure in her voice, making it a statement of fact rather than criticism.

'Not yet.' His tone was low too. 'I'm a poor loser, haven't you found that out? What's mine I like to keep.'

'You're making me sound like a possession again,' she said reproachfully.

He shook his head and pulled his lips down in a rueful gesture. 'That wasn't my intention. You're not an object, Sapphire, you're my wife—a warm, responsive, sexy woman, who I was a fool to ever let walk out on me.'

'So why did you?' she asked. 'I gave you fair warning; why didn't you do something about it?'

'I didn't think you meant it,' he said regretfully. 'I didn't think anyone as physically responsive as you could turn your back on what we had.'

'If you think sex was all I needed then you don't know me as well as you think you do,' she returned.

There was no animosity in their words, they were each stating the facts as they saw them, and Sapphire had the feeling that it was a beginning, that they were at last learning to communicate. Perhaps this was something that had been sadly missing in their marriage. Drake had been too busy to give her the time she needed and wanted, and instead of talking to him rationally about it she had become resentful, harbouring her feelings, attacking instead of reasoning, making things worse instead of better.

'Maybe I don't,' he confessed. 'But it's something I intend to remedy, and whether it takes place here or at home is up to you. I've enjoyed this evening very much, Sapphire. Perhaps it's an indication of things to come?'

Sapphire smiled weakly. It was far too soon to say. She had enjoyed the last few hours as well, but she was not so sure that Drake was a patient enough man to go along indefinitely at such a slow pace. Everything he did he did in a hurry. Even their romance had been rushed. He had scarcely given her time to breathe before he'd suggested marriage, and she had been so infatuated with him that she had agreed straight away.

Infatuated! Now why had that word sprung into her mind? Shouldn't it have been love? Hadn't she been *in love* with him? Confusion returned. All of a sudden she did not know what to think any more. Maybe she'd been in love with an ideal? A man with money? Heavens, it didn't bear thinking about. 'I think I'd like to go to bed,' she said quietly.

Drake nodded. 'A good idea.'

They returned to the house together and Sapphire went upstairs. He didn't even kiss her again. Incredibly she fell asleep straight away, and the next morning was amazed that her muddled and uneasy thoughts hadn't kept her awake.

She brushed her teeth and showered, and realised with a pang that she quite liked having Drake's toothbrush next to hers, and his shaving cream and razor on the windowsill. The scent of his musky aftershave still hung in the air, and he was with her in spirit even before she joined him downstairs.

Smells of a different kind assailed her nostrils—crispy bacon and sizzling sausages, fried mushrooms and egg. She decided she could quite get used to being looked after like this.

'Good morning, my darling.' Drake's smile was wide and enveloping, though he made no attempt to cross the room and kiss her. 'Did you sleep well?'

'Wonderfully so.'

'I hope you're hungry?'

'Amazingly, yes.' Normally she never ate anything other than toast and marmalade, but having breakfast cooked for her made all the difference. If Drake was trying to make amends he was succeeding. The saying that the way to a man's heart was through his stomach could almost be reversed.

'Then if you'd like to take your seat outside, breakfast will be served in a few minutes,' he said cheerfully.

Through the window Sapphire noted that he had covered the old wooden table with a cloth, and knives and forks were already in place. It was blue skies yet again and perfect for eating al fresco, but she could not help wondering whether any of this was for Robin's benefit. Drake must know her neighbour could see them.

But she said nothing, going outside and sitting down, helping herself to chilled orange juice which he must have bought that morning because she knew there was none in the refrigerator. Every window next door was closed, making her wonder whether Robin had gone away, whether having her husband as a neighbour was more than he could stand. She felt sorry for him and was disappointed he had said nothing to her.

'Madam, your breakfast.' Drake, still in his jovial mood, walked out with a tray and placed a plate in front of her. They ate for a few minutes in silence, until Drake said, 'Today I think we'll go——'

'I have films to develop,' cut in Sapphire quickly.

A sudden frown took the place of his smile. 'But surely they can wait. Nothing can be that important.'

'Wasn't your work important when you kept leaving me to amuse myself?'

'Yes, but that's different.'

'It's not different at all,' objected Sapphire. 'This is my job, a full-time one, it pays for the roof over my head—I can't keep taking days off.'

'Of course—I'd forgotten.'

She did not like his sudden smile of acquiescence. It was unlike Drake to give in so easily. Then she remembered their conversation last night and the way he had seemed to be trying to put things right between them, and she smiled graciously herself. 'I'll try to do them as quickly as I can,' she told him.

'It's all right.' He lifted his wide, muscular shoulders. 'I understand what the pressure of work is like,' and he continued to eat his bacon and egg.

Sapphire spent all morning in her darkroom, and became so engrossed that all thoughts of Drake fled. The photographs of the orchids were among some of the best she had ever taken, and the harbour scenes were delightful.

When Drake tapped on her door to announce that lunch was ready she could not believe it was that time already. 'I can't leave what I'm doing just yet,' she called out. 'I'll eat later. Have yours, don't wait for me.' The next moment he was again forgotten.

When she finally emerged, stiff and tired but extremely satisfied with her day's work, Sapphire found Drake asleep on her sun-lounger in the garden, shirt discarded, hard-muscled chest rising and falling steadily. How often that same body had been pressed close to hers, and how tempting it was to touch him now.

But she resisted the urge and found her lunch, a cold chicken salad, in the fridge. She had just sat down to eat when the telephone rang.

'Sapphire, I won't beat about the bush.' It was Lorna Brecon's high-pitched voice. 'I know I told you you could live in my cottage for as long as you liked, but circumstances have changed and I——'

'You're going to sell it,' Sapphire put in quickly. 'Yes, I know, Caroline told me. I've been thinking about it, Lorna, and if you're not asking too much I'd like to buy it myself.'

There was a slight pause, then Lorna answered regretfully, 'Oh, dear, I'm afraid that's impossible. It's already been sold.'

Sapphire's mouth dropped open in shock. 'I didn't realise you'd put it on the market yet. I thought if I got in quickly I——'

'I haven't,' said Lorna. 'But—well, I had an offer too good to refuse, so I'm afraid I'm going to have to ask you to get out as soon as you can.'

'How soon?' There was something about Lorna's tone that had an ominous ring to it.

'By the end of the week.'

'But—but——' Sapphire was stuck for words. 'That's not possible. House sales don't go through that quickly.'

'This man has influence, and money,' insisted Lorna. 'He wants the property and he wants it now. He's paying cash.'

Sapphire shook her head. 'This is unbelievable.'

'I thought so myself, but I'd be a fool to turn him down.'

An icy cold shiver ran down Sapphire's spine, a gut feeling, a sudden suspicion. 'What's this man's name?' she asked.

There was a little silence at the other end. 'I'm not allowed to divulge it, not yet, not until the sale has actually gone through.'

'It's Drake, isn't it?' burst out Sapphire angrily. 'My husband's the swine who's done this. My God, I knew he wanted me out of here, but I didn't think he'd go to these lengths. Thanks for telling me, Lorna.' She slammed the receiver down, already debating what her plan of action should be.

CHAPTER EIGHT

SAPPHIRE was given no chance to dwell on Lorna's bombshell. Drake walked in, and it was obvious by his expression that he had heard every word of her conversation. 'So now you have no excuse not to come home with me.' His smile was triumphant.

With eyes glaring Sapphire launched into her attack. 'God, you're the most devious, cunning swine I've ever met. What are you going to do with the cottage, let it out to someone else, or keep it for yourself and use it as a love-nest?' Her tone rang with anger and her eyes flashed with very real hatred.

He had been so nice to her last night, yet all the time he had known she was going to have to move out; it had all been planned. He must have got in touch with Lorna yesterday and fixed the whole thing up.

'I have a friend who's been looking for a cottage down here for a long time,' he said with some satisfaction. 'I'm letting it to him. He's moving in on Monday.'

Sapphire felt like slapping his face, knocking some of the complacency out of him. She shook her head wildly. 'I really can't credit that you're forcing me out, Drake.' Even though he had said in the beginning that he would find some way of terminating her tenancy she hadn't believed he would be so unscrupulous. What alternative had she now but to go home with him? She could find somewhere else, of course, but it wouldn't be easy, and she certainly couldn't manage it by the end of the week. He truly had her cornered.

'Oh, I am, believe me,' he said, still with that infuriating smile curving his lips. 'It was really extraordinarily easy. Lorna Brecon was delighted with the offer I made. Although force is rather a harsh word; it suggests violence, Sapphire. My methods are more refined than that.'

'Refined?' she yelled. 'Unprincipled, sneaky, conniving, dishonourable, deceitful, yes, but refined? Never! I always thought you were a gentleman, Drake; now I know you're nothing of the kind. It's all a veneer. It makes me wonder whether I've ever met the true you. You have so many guises that I'm left in a constant state of confusion. How are you going to get the sale through so quickly?'

He lifted his shoulders in an easy gesture. 'I have friends in the right places. There's nothing that can't be achieved if you put your mind to it.'

Sapphire felt herself actually trembling with anger. Was it only yesterday that she had decided she did not want to stay here, that she had considered going home with Drake? She had gone to bed last night feeling wonderful, she had woken up this morning feeling the same, feeling that at long last she and Drake were on the way to a definite reconciliation. Now she wished him a thousand miles away, and the thought of sharing his home was abhorrent. Was this really the man she had married? This man who was capable of trickery of the lowest sort to get his own way?

'This is all some sort of game to you, isn't it?' she asked furiously. 'You think it's funny turning me out of my home. I don't happen to share your opinion. If I had somewhere else to go I would, you can bet your bottom dollar on that, but as I haven't, I seem to have no choice but to go back to Treetops. You can rest assured, however, that I shall stay no longer than is necessary to find myself somewhere else to live. My opinion of you at this moment is at rock bottom.'

'You're very beautiful when you're angry, even more so than usual.' He was completely unperturbed by her anger. 'Your eyes, your lovely eyes, sparkle like real sapphires, and I can think of a much better way to spend that passion. It's wasted in hostility.'

'Really?' Sapphire drew in a much-needed breath, standing tall and straight and glaring her fury. 'I'm afraid you've cooked your goose. I don't want you touching me, let alone making love to me. Is that clear?'

If she hadn't been watching him closely she would have missed the brief tightening of his features, the flicker of pain in his eyes. It was gone in an instant, replaced again by the confident smile. But it pleased her that she had managed to get through to him, that she had hurt him even if only in some small way. He deserved it.

'People always say things they don't mean when they're angry,' he stated with complete confidence.

Her fine brows rose. 'I mean every word. You might have won in one direction, but certainly not the other. You're going to wish you'd never gone to all this trouble. Whatever you've paid for this cottage is going to be a whole lot of wasted money.'

'We'll see about that,' he grinned. 'Why don't you finish your lunch?'

'I don't want it,' she snapped. 'I just want to be left alone. Get out of here, will you?'

He shrugged and with a great show of reluctance began to walk out of the room. In the doorway he turned. 'If I were you I'd start packing. I see no point in hanging on until the end of the week.'

Sapphire picked up the nearest thing which came to hand and hurled it at him. He sidestepped easily, and the heavy book hit the wall and crashed harmlessly to the floor.

'Tut, tut,' he mocked. 'You really ought to keep a curb on your temper—it doesn't become you at all.'

'The longer I live with you the worse it's going to get,' she screamed. 'This really is an impossible situation. I don't see how you think it can work. We're not compatible, I don't know why we got married in the first place. We should have got to know each other better before committing ourselves—it would have saved us both a lot of heartache.'

'Is that what you really think, Sapphire——' a frown took the place of his smile, furrowing his brow and narrowing his eyes '—that we're not compatible?'

'Most definitely,' she whipped back. 'Getting married to you was the biggest mistake of my life. There's only one thing I want now, and that's to get out of it.'

'You're not prepared to give it another go?' Drake was serious now.

Sapphire shook her head. 'It will be a waste of time.'

'I don't happen to share your opinion. I think it could work. Give me three months, Sapphire, that's all I'm asking. If we haven't sorted ourselves out by then I'll give you your divorce.'

Going back to Treetops was the most difficult thing Sapphire had ever had to do, it was worse even than when she left Drake, because then she had been starting a new life; now she could see nothing stretching ahead of her except three months of sheer torment.

She had insisted on having separate bedrooms, and now, two weeks into their so-called truce, things were no better than they had been at the beginning.

As much as she could Sapphire ignored her husband. She made sure that her photography took up most of her time. It wasn't difficult; it had become a part of her life, and she had a lot of work lined up.

Even though Drake was spending his evenings at home she contrarily spent hers in her newly set up darkroom. Let him have a taste of his own medicine, she thought bitterly, see how he liked it. She was still smarting from his treatment of her; she did not take kindly to being kicked out of the home she had made for herself.

Robin had been furious when she told him. 'You don't have to go back with him—you can move in with me,' he spluttered. But Sapphire knew that Drake was quite capable of using force if he had to, of picking her up and carrying her off, and she told Robin as much.

'It wouldn't help matters. You've no idea what Drake's like once he's made up his mind about something.'

The whole thing had to be done civilly, and if it meant living with him for the next three months then that was what she would do, but she had no intention of meeting him even halfway. She still resented the way he had erupted back into her life and taken over. He seemed to think that because she was still legally his wife it gave him some sort of right.

Drake let it go on for another week before he lost his patience altogether. Sapphire emerged from her darkroom one evening to find him outside her door, his hand raised as though he were just about to push it open. For a couple of seconds they eyed each other mutinously, then he said in a voice tight with suppressed anger, 'This has to stop. Surely there are enough hours in the day for you to do your damn developing without using the evenings as well?'

Sapphire looked steadfastly back at him. 'It bothers you, does it?'

'It most certainly does. I call it a most uncivilised way of going on. We should be spending our evenings together. How are we going to mend our marriage if you spend all your time avoiding me?'

'You tell me,' she thrust scathingly. 'I had two years of it, don't forget, and I wasn't supposed to mind, I was supposed to take it all in good grace, find myself something to do or somewhere to go. I suggest you do the same.'

Drake turned away so that Sapphire was unable to see the expression on his face. 'You really know how to hit below the belt, don't you?' he asked gruffly.

'Do you accept that it's the truth?'

He heaved a sigh and looked back at her. 'I hadn't realised how much it was destroying you.'

'Oh, you destroyed me all right,' she yelled. 'You've destroyed every little bit of love I felt for you. The truth is, Drake, I can't wait for the end of the three months. All I can say is thank goodness I have my work to stop me going insane.'

He clenched his teeth and said nothing for several long seconds. 'You're not giving us a chance, Sapphire.'

'Neither did you,' she snapped.

'*Touché*,' he conceded, 'but I'm willing to try now, I'm willing to admit that I've made some mistakes. What else do you want me to do, go down on my hands and knees and grovel?'

'I can't see you going that.'

'No, you're damn right I wouldn't, but I would like to spend some time with you.'

'I'll see what I can manage,' she said.

Drake's roar of anger startled her. 'You'll see what you can manage! Dammit, Sapphire, this has gone on long enough. You're my wife, and I want to spend some time with you. We'll go out for a meal tomorrow night, and the next day I intend to ask Marie and Eric over.

They've been badgering me ever since we got back together.'

She looked at him sharply. 'Do you have to invite your parents?' There were sure to be recriminations for her walking out on Drake, and this was the last thing she wanted. The tension of living with him was more than enough to cope with for the time being.

'Of course I have to,' he snarled. 'If I don't they'll begin to wonder whether you really are back home. I never thought of you as an unreasonable woman, until now. What the hell is it with you, Sapphire, that you won't meet me halfway?'

'I can't believe you need to ask. You know what's wrong.'

'You're going to behave like a stranger for the next three months, is that what you're saying?' His light blue eyes were hard, his whole body filled with tension. 'You're going to ignore me, you're going to pretend I'm not here. You go your way, I go mine, is that it?'

'Something like that,' she agreed. 'It's much as we were doing in the very beginning.'

'Damn you, Sapphire!' he grated. 'This is a totally different situation. You're being deliberately awkward. My work was too important to neglect.'

'More important than your marriage?'

His lips twisted angrily. 'You're determined to rub it in, aren't you? I've admitted I was in the wrong—what more do you want? Do you want me to swear it'll never happen again, is that it? Do you want apology piled on apology? Are you never going to let me forget it?' He breathed out heavily and swung away, turning his back on her and moving a few paces before spinning around again and eyeing her savagely.

'If you think that because of your inflexible attitude I'll change my mind, you're mistaken,' he went on. 'Our agreement was for three months, and that still stands. It can be happy or miserable, Sapphire, it's up to you. But I won't have any more of this shutting yourself away, is that clear? You're to spend your evenings with me.'

Sapphire eyed him mutinously, but did not argue. She lifted her shoulders in an indifferent shrug. 'It sounds like a whole heap of fun.'

The irony behind her words made him draw in a swift, hissing breath of anger and he lurched towards her. 'Damn you, Sapphire, what the hell's going through that warped mind of yours?' He took her by her upper arms, fingers gripping and bruising. 'We're supposed to be attempting a reconciliation, not fighting a battle.'

'Let's say I don't like your methods.' Her eyes glared into his, and if it were possible for sparks to fly out of them they would have done. 'You forced me into coming here, you made me leave my home and my friends. I shan't forgive you easily for that.'

His eyes narrowed and there was a sudden chill in the atmosphere. 'You're missing Robin, is that what's wrong? Is that where your mind is when you shut me out? Dammit, Sapphire, he has no part in your life. I won't let him—you're mine so long as there's a piece of paper that says you are.'

'You're hurting me, Drake.' Sapphire kept her tone low and looked at him coolly. 'And you're barking up the wrong tree if you think Robin's the reason for my behaviour. *You* are the reason, you and no one else.' Maybe she was being hard on him, but all she knew was that she needed her own space until she had sorted herself out.

He let her go, but he did not move away. He looked down at her with steady eyes that imprisoned her as much as his hands had. 'What went wrong, Sapphire? Was it really because of my work, or have you never truly loved me?'

'I thought I loved you when I married you,' she whispered, aware of the sudden change in the atmosphere, 'but then you were away such a lot, and—and after I left you I didn't know what I felt any more. I'm still not sure.'

Anger tightened his jaw for several long seconds, then he visibly relaxed. 'Perhaps this will help.' He cupped her face, lowering his head and pressing his lips to hers.

A few seconds was all Sapphire allowed herself, a few seconds' delirious pleasure. It was the first time Drake had kissed her since they had come home, and it was the sweet nectar of life, but it was emotional blackmail and not the answer to their problems.

'No, Drake.' She jerked away from him, her eyes wide in her pale face. 'It will solve nothing.'

'Because you know that you want me as much as I want you? Have you any idea what it's cost me this last few weeks to keep away from you?'

'I don't care what it's cost you,' she retorted. 'There's no question that we're compatible physically. The question is whether we could ever live harmoniously together again. As things stand at this moment, I doubt it very much. We're so different, you and I, we want different things out of life.'

'I want us to be happy.'

Sapphire gave a bitter smile. 'If only that were as easy as it sounds. There are so many different aspects of happiness, and we had none of them.'

His frown was harsh and incredulous. 'How can you say that?'

'Would I have left you if I'd been happy?'

'You had everything money could buy. Wasn't that what you wanted?'

'It's what *you* thought I wanted,' she returned viciously. 'Money is an evil. I used to think it would be an advantage—oh, yes, I admit that, but I was wrong, very wrong. I was happier living at home in poverty than I ever was with you.'

Drake winced at her cruel words. 'And yet you still enjoy spending it.' His tone was caustic now, burning into her, deliberately hurting. Sapphire closed her eyes. Now was the time to tell him she had spent it all on her mother, but before she could speak he continued, 'I suggest you have a good long think tonight, Sapphire, because starting tomorrow I want no more of this non-sense. I don't mind you doing your photography, it's good that you have something to interest you, but not when I'm at home. We're going to work on our re-lationship, do everything in our power to mend our failed marriage.'

He walked quickly away, and Sapphire stood looking after him. Did this mean that he did care something for her after all? That perhaps he did love her in his own way, even though he had never put it into words? Perhaps the time had come to unbend a little, to see whether they could rescue anything of their marriage. There was an awful lot of talking to do, a lot of things to sort out, but the future was beginning to look faintly hopeful.

For the first time since coming home Sapphire lay awake in her bed wishing Drake was sharing it with her. She had managed to shut him out of her mind while there was a distance between them, but that brief kiss had awoken dangerous feelings, and it would be so easy to give in to him. She actually felt quite alarmed by the sensations tingling through her veins, the ache in the pit of her stomach that only he could assuage.

It was wrong, she knew, to want him like this when the other side of their marriage was completely out of order, wrong to indulge in the carnal side of it when true friendship, contentment in each other's company, wanting to be together at all times, and above all having children, was unattainable.

Drake had already left for the office when she got up the next morning. It was the first time this had happened since he had brought her home, and she frowned faintly when she saw the empty kitchen. He was usually in there drinking tea and reading the morning's newspaper. Painful memories returned of that other morning when he had walked out and not come back.

She filled the kettle, popped bread into the toaster, then saw his note propped against the teapot.

> Something's cropped up, Sapphire. I may be late back tonight. It *would* happen at a time like this, but it can't be helped. Don't wait up for me, and don't forget my parents are coming tomorrow. They'll be here for lunch and I'm hoping to take the day off—provided this problem is resolved.
>
> Yours as always,
> Drake

Sapphire shook her head in disbelief as she read it. Something had cropped up, had it? Something no one else could handle? She screwed the piece of paper into a ball and threw it savagely across the kitchen. So much for good resolutions. They certainly hadn't lasted very long—and this wouldn't be the first time he would let her down. Drake hated not being in charge. He liked to be there where the action was. It must have crucified him this last three weeks.

And what did he mean, yours as always? Yours what? In love? In friendship? In haste? In anger? She was furious. Why couldn't he have woken her? Why did he have to leave a note? Why couldn't he have told her himself?

Words on a page were so impersonal. Who knew what his feelings were as he wrote them? A kiss and an apology and seeing in his eyes that he was truly sorry would have been so much better. Perhaps he wasn't sorry? Perhaps her attitude had got to him so much that he was glad of an excuse to stay out? Except that he had said last night he wanted her with him. None of it made sense.

The kettle boiled and she made a mug of tea and buttered her toast, but she left it half finished on the plate. She had a photographic assignment at a large private country manor, whose owners intended opening their gardens to the public next year and wished to produce a glossy brochure for advance publicity, and she was thankful for something to take her mind off Drake.

Although the morning had started out with blue skies, by noon it was raining heavily. Sapphire would have preferred to call it a day, but Mr and Mrs Langston insisted that she stay for lunch. They were hoping it would clear up and she could continue, but when it was still raining at two Sapphire thanked them very much and went home, arranging to return the following week.

She was not surprised when Drake failed to return, and when there was still no sign of him by ten o'clock she went to bed. It reminded her of the early days of their marriage, and she knew this would not be a one-off occasion. After all the fuss he had made yesterday about her working during the evenings he was now doing the very same thing.

For a long time she lay listening for his return, and it was after midnight when she finally fell asleep. When she awoke the next morning she felt vaguely worried, but it was not for a few minutes that she worked out the reason why.

Rosemarie and Eric were coming to lunch! She had to cook a meal and entertain them and pretend there was nothing wrong, pretend that her marriage was back on an even keel, that she and Drake had resolved all their problems and were now happy together. And there was every possibility that she would have to do it on her own! Drake might still be needed at the office—or in whichever part of the country it was that he had gone. In fact, she was still not sure whether he had returned last night.

She threw back the covers, took a shower and washed her hair, and when she went downstairs Drake was in the kitchen. He looked tired and drawn, but he smiled and came across the room to kiss her. 'Good morning, my love.'

She could have rebuffed him, but in effect she was glad of the chance to pretend that everything was all right between them. It would make the whole day so much easier. So she returned his kiss and sat down at the table and let him pour her tea and make her toast. 'What time did you get home?' she asked.

He brushed a hand wearily through his hair. 'Long gone midnight. Some fool fouled up an order and the wrong furniture was delivered. It was actually installed before anyone realised the mistake. It wouldn't have mattered, except that it was for some prestigious office block being opened officially today. How we got the right stuff there in time I'll never know. We all worked our guts out, and then I drove like mad to get back here. I knew you wouldn't want to face Marie and Eric on your own.

His thoughtfulness astonished Sapphire. For so long he hadn't cared whether he stayed out all night or not; she had entertained his parents several times by herself. 'Thank you,' she said quietly. 'I must confess I'm not looking forward to it.'

'They're eager to give us their blessing,' he told her quietly. 'They were devastated when we split up.'

'It's a little premature, don't you think?' There was a sudden sharp edge to her tone which she could not help.

Drake frowned. 'I naturally haven't told them all the facts. They presume that everything's all right between us.'

Sapphire shook her head. 'I don't see how any broken relationship can get back on the same footing. There must always be some residue of the conditions that split the couple up in the first place.'

'It's hard work, yes, I agree,' he said, 'but people manage it—and I want us to, Sapphire. I don't want you to do or say anything today that will make my parents think otherwise.'

Sapphire closed her eyes. He really was asking the impossible.

'Is something wrong?' His tone was suddenly sharp, and when she looked at him he was frowning.

'It's going to be hard for me,' she said huskily.

He touched his hand to hers. 'Marie's very fond of you. I think you're looking for problems that aren't there. Whatever you do I don't want you upsetting her. She has this heart condition, and——'

'I didn't know that,' cut in Sapphire sharply. 'You've never told me.'

'Because I'm not supposed to know,' Drake returned with a rueful grimace. 'Marie swore Eric to silence because she thought I had enough problems of my own, but it wasn't the sort of thing he could keep to himself for ever.'

'Has she been ill long?' asked Sapphire with a worried frown.'

Drake drew in a deep breath. 'The doctors seem to think she may have had this problem longer than anyone knew, but it didn't manifest itself until——' he hesitated, and then went on reluctantly '—until you walked out on me.'

Sapphire gasped. 'Are you saying I'm to blame? That it's me who caused it?' A cold chill stole over her. This was terrible. She had never dreamt that leaving Drake would affect other people's lives besides their own. Dear heaven, how was she ever going to live with this knowledge?

'Any sort of shock could have triggered it, Sapphire; you mustn't blame yourself,' he said gently. 'Nevertheless, you can see now why it wouldn't be wise to let her see that there's anything wrong, and for goodness' sake don't get all worked up and let Marie know that you know. She hates people fussing over her.'

'I wish you'd told me before,' she grumbled.

'I wouldn't have told you now if you weren't kicking up such a fuss about them coming. Don't let me down, Sapphire.' He took her hands and as their eyes met she felt her heart lurch.

How easy it was to respond to him, to give way to the emotions she tried desperately hard to keep in check. She was still uncertain whether she truly loved him, whether she had ever loved him at all—no, that was wrong, she had loved him, but was it the right kind of love? Were they both guilty of feeling nothing more than physical attraction? Lovemaking had certainly been the best part of their marriage; everything else had fallen apart.

There had been a time at the cottage when they had begun to talk, when she had felt that they were learning to communicate and that perhaps their problems could be sorted out. And then came Lorna's devastating phone call, and not surprisingly they had never got back on the same footing; they were each on the defensive, ready to jump down each other's throats instead of calmly discussing their grievances.

Sapphire was aware of the fact that she was as guilty as Drake of not confessing her true state of mind; it was just so difficult to know where to begin, especially as she was not sure what his deep-down feelings were. If only he would say something, if only he would open his heart to her. Why did he let her go on thinking he was interested in her for sex's sake alone?

'I suggest we finish our breakfast.' He squeezed her fingers and pressed a kiss to her brow, his eyes shadowed, as though he were reluctant to let her go. Sapphire was tempted to slide her arms around him and offer up her mouth, but almost before the thought was born she was free, and the moment passed.

Once breakfast was over Drake disappeared into his study and Sapphire prepared everything as far as she could for their lunch. She had never felt more nervous about a meal, and she hoped she would be able to cope. She truly was grateful that Drake had taken the day off.

Shortly before Marie and Eric were due to arrive she changed into a jade-green dress that Drake had bought her in the early days of their marriage. It was in a soft, silky material, and he had encouraged her to wear it around the house with no bra or pants. In those days she hadn't minded. It had made her feel sexy and vulnerable, and he had told her she was irresistible and magical and they had always ended up making love.

This wasn't the reason she put it on today. It was a cool, attractive dress and she felt good in it, and she needed this boost to her morale to face his parents. There were sure to be questions asked about their separation, and she did not want to let Drake down; this was the perfect dress for the occasion. She wasn't expecting him to come to her bedroom, though, and she spun around in surprise when she heard the door open.

'I wondered whether you were ready. You've been up here so long I thought you might be getting cold feet.'

'I'm ready now,' said Sapphire softly, walking towards the door, trying to still the tremors that ran through her. Drake had changed too, into a pair of blue mohair trousers and an ice-blue shirt that matched his eyes. He had showered and his hair was still crisp and damp; her heart skittered just looking at him. He made no attempt to move away from the door, appraising Sapphire thoroughly as she neared him, seeking each curve, seeming to see right through the dress to her trembling body beneath.

'This isn't how I remember you wearing it,' he muttered thickly as his hands came out to stroke the soft swell of her breasts. 'This dress wasn't made to be worn with anything underneath,' he added as his hands slid around her waist and moved down over her taut buttocks. 'This type of fabric should drape only naked skin. Didn't it feel far more sensual when you wore it that way?'

Sapphire swallowed and nodded. Already the old feelings were crowding back, her whole body tingling with sensation and need and an aching desire to be made love to. Here, now, this very minute.

CHAPTER NINE

UNCONSCIOUSLY Sapphire moved her body against Drake's, recreating in part the love-play they had always enjoyed. It was so easy to shut her eyes and pretend that there was nothing wrong, that all the aching months of separation had never happened, that his propensity for work, his affair with another woman, had not pushed them apart. Together, like this, their bodies moving rhythmically, it was so easy to forget their differences.

'I can't wear it like that in front of Marie and Eric,' she protested huskily.

'Then I'll forgive you on this occasion,' he murmured against her ear. 'But I want you to promise that you'll wear it for me again like you used to.'

'When the time's right,' she agreed. If his parents weren't coming, now would be right. She felt so aroused, so ready for him, and he must know it. Why had he chosen this moment to awaken her most primitive feelings? Or was it her own fault because she had worn this dress? Had she subconsciously tried to tell him that she was ready for more from him?

On the other hand, why had he come to her room? He had not known what she was going to wear. Normally, if he wanted her, he tapped the door, but he never invaded her privacy. He went along with the rules she had imposed.

'Then I'll have to make sure the time is right very soon,' he announced thickly, his arms tightening, his mouth seeking and finding hers. 'I can't wait for you much longer, Sapphire.'

Her lips parted eagerly, accepting his kiss, responding with complete abandonment. The years slipped away; it was as though they had never been apart, as though nothing had happened to upset the perfect harmony they had felt in the first blissful weeks of marriage.

Their mutual hunger was only partially satisfied. Time was their enemy. 'Not now, my love,' breathed Drake, his breath warm and fresh against her mouth. 'Not now; making love is too precious to rush. Although——' he added with a wry smile '—if my parents knew what we were doing I'm sure they'd forgive us if lunch was late.'

'I'd be too embarrassed to serve it,' confessed Sapphire.

'Embarrassed at something so natural? My darling Sapphire, that doesn't sound like the girl I married at all. Remember how eager you were to make love all the time? I used to say you were addicted to it, and you didn't care who saw you with that look on your face that's so unmistakable. A woman who's been well and truly loved is a joy to behold.'

Sapphire knew what he meant. She had seen herself in the mirror; her face glowing, her eyes sparkling, her lips soft and faintly swollen. She had looked beautiful, and anyone observing her would have known the reason for it. 'I still don't want Marie and Eric to see me like that,' she whispered.

Drake inclined his head. 'Then I'll await the pleasure; later perhaps, when they've gone? While you're still wearing this dress; before you turn the cold shoulder on me again. Oh, God, Sapphire, have you any idea what you're doing to me?'

Had he any idea what he was doing to her? The thought of him making love to her later was enough to send her into a spin. She suddenly wanted it very much, and to hell with the consequences. If lunch was a success it would be amazing.

On the surface nothing had changed. Marie expressed her pleasure that Sapphire and Drake had got back together and was as friendly and affectionate as she had ever been. There were no recriminations, as Sapphire had feared, no questions asked, just quiet, happy acceptance that they were reunited.

Throughout the meal Drake's eyes were on her often, though whether he was thinking about making love to her later, or making sure she said nothing to upset Marie, Sapphire could not be certain. Whatever, it had the effect of keeping her feelings running high—and also reassuring his parents that everything was all right between them.

When they finished eating Eric asked Drake to show him the garden and Marie offered to help Sapphire clear the table. Drake gave her a warning glance as they left the room, but he did not have to worry. She had no intention of saying anything. She could not live with upsetting Marie again.

'I'm so pleased to see the two of you looking so happy,' said Marie once they were alone. 'I couldn't believe it when Drake first told us you'd left him. It was a great shock—you were so suited, what on earth went wrong? He'd never talk about it.'

Sapphire was surprised Drake had said nothing, but pleased too. She hadn't liked to think of him talking about her, maybe running her down. 'I think I wasn't ready for marriage,' she confessed, slotting plates into the dishwasher. 'I couldn't cope. Perhaps we hadn't known each other long enough—I don't know.'

'So long as you're all right now, that's the main thing,' said Marie.

'It's still early days,' said Sapphire quietly, 'but I'm hoping it will eventually work out. We have a lot of talking to do and—oh, I don't know, Marie, but it's so difficult. There are things I want to say, but I can't seem to find the right time or the right words.'

'You must make the time,' Marie told her wisely. 'The longer you leave it the worse it will be, until it becomes impossible to talk at all. The very fact that you've agreed to give your marriage another go must mean that you love my son.'

My son! It was good that she thought of Drake like that, and Sapphire really admired her for taking Drake in as she had and giving him a home. It was understandable that she had been hurt when his marriage went wrong.

'If I could have chosen a wife for Drake it would have been you, Sapphire,' Marie went on. 'I welcomed you with open arms as my daughter-in-law. I was devastated when he told us you'd left him.'

'I'm sorry you were upset,' said Sapphire.

'My thoughts have been with you, my darling. Drake's a good man, even though he's a workaholic. Who knows? Maybe your separation has done him good, given him the jolt he needed. I believe he's not working half the long hours he used to?'

'No, he isn't.'

Marie smiled, satisfied. 'I have a feeling that everything's going to be all right.'

Sapphire wished she could be as sure.

Eventually the conversation turned to other subjects, and when the kitchen was clean and tidy they went back outside to join the men. Not long afterwards Eric said they must be making a move.

They weren't driving back to London but carrying on to spend a few days with friends. In the past they had stayed here, and Sapphire did not see any reason why they shouldn't now. She could only surmise that they thought it prudent to give them both breathing space.

'That wasn't as bad as I expected,' she said, once she and Drake were alone. They were sitting in her favourite room, the french windows open, their two chairs facing the garden. It was warm, but not quite warm enough to sit outside.

'You and Marie always did get on well,' commented Drake.

Sapphire nodded.

'You didn't say anything to upset her?'

'Of course not. We did talk about you and me, but she wasn't distressed, merely handing out advice—you know the sort of thing mothers do.'

He nodded. 'Eric was much the same—but I can think of far more important things to talk about than my parents. How I kept my hands off you throughout the meal I've no idea.' His voice deepened, became throaty and sensual. 'You're more beautiful than ever, Sapphire, so lovely, so totally irresistible.'

He still made no attempt to touch her, but his eyes held hers, and there was no hiding his desire. Sapphire felt an instant response, felt her whole body grow warm with need, and it was all she could do to stop herself from moving into his arms.

It would be so easy at this moment—and yet she knew it still wasn't the right time. Once she let him make love to her there would be no going back. He would expect a commitment, he would expect far more from her than she was prepared to give. She did not want to settle into the same sort of lifestyle that they had had before; she wanted children, a family around her, everything that Drake didn't want.

She could not face a barren future, even though she had thought so at one time. It was something they needed to discuss. Perhaps she was afraid of what he would say, perhaps that was why she was always reluctant to raise the subject. On the other hand, he never invited that type of conversation; all he was interested in was making love. It had always been that way—whenever he came home he wanted to make love, no mention of actually being in love with her, just satiating his hunger.

She gave him a wry smile. 'I'm flattered that you find me irresistible, but I have films that need urgently developing.'

'Oh, no, you don't!' It was the growl of a lion being threatened. 'You're not shutting yourself away up there—you've done enough of that recently. I want your company, Sapphire, and I intend to have it. The rest of this day is for me.'

'So what shall we do?' she asked with forced cheerfulness, immediately giving up on the idea of working. It had been a means of getting away from Drake, but it wasn't worth making an issue over.

'You know damn well what I want to do.' Drake moved closer and compelled her to look at him, his light blue eyes simmering with naked desire.

Sapphire took a step backwards, shaking her head. 'I'm not going to let you make love to me.'

A harsh frown abruptly carved his brow. 'I've waited long enough, my lovely wife. My patience is at a very thin ebb. And don't say you don't want it as much as me, because I know you do. It's there on your face, in your eyes—it's been there all day. You're as hungry for me as I am for you.'

But sex for the sake of sex wasn't what she wanted at all. The way she looked at things, it was wrong for him to want to make love when the mood suddenly came upon him. In an ideal marriage they ought to feel at one with each other the whole time, always aware, always conscious of each other's needs, so that at any single time they could make love and not feel it was something done in the heat of the moment. Making love, she thought, should be an expression of continuous feelings, not an act of sudden passion. She did not want to be simply a sex object. She closed her eyes. How on earth was she going to make Drake understand that?

Sapphire did not hear him move, she knew nothing until she felt his hard body against hers, his arms pinning her ruthlessly to him, his breath warm on her cheek. 'Let's see if your body denies me,' he whispered.

He must have known it wouldn't, he must have known that her overheated limbs would give away her secret. The moment his mouth claimed hers was the moment of her undoing.

'It's been far too long, Sapphire,' he groaned. 'You can't go on denying me like this. My body's only human, it won't stand any more.'

She resisted for a few seconds only before helplessly returning his kisses, feeding her hunger, glorying in his exciting maleness so close to her. It was wrong and right at the same time. She ignited as instantly as dry tinder.

Forgotten, overpowering feelings assailed her, stunning her with their force, making her realise that not only had she been punishing Drake but herself too. She had been missing this intense, sensual pleasure for some stubborn, foolish reason that at this particular moment in time eluded her. This man was her husband and she wanted him—and he wanted her! What could be simpler?

The zip on the back of her dress was pulled down, the silky material slid from her shoulders. Her bra was dispensed with next, and surprisingly she felt his fingers trembling as he undressed her.

She could understand his trepidation. Although it was nothing new, although he had done it dozens of times before, it had a different feel to it, more of a thrill, more anticipation, caused by not altogether knowing what to expect.

'My darling Sapphire,' he muttered thickly, 'you're a thousand times more beautiful than I remember. A little thinner, perhaps——' he touched her waist and hips '—but still infinitely desirable.' His hands trailed upwards, reaching her breasts already swollen and aching, her nipples tightly erect. He stroked with feather-light fingertips, increasing her torment, then he lowered his head and gently took each aching nipple in turn into his mouth.

How he could be so gentle she did not know. He had spoken of unfulfilled hunger; she had expected him to fall on her ravenously. But his touch was, strangely, all the more exciting because of its lightness, his tongue rasping and tasting, his teeth delicately biting, his fingers holding and stroking.

She clutched his head to her, an unconscious moan escaping the back of her throat. It was exquisite torture, and a helpless longing filled her. 'Oh, Drake!' she murmured. 'Oh, Drake!'

He lifted his head. 'You feel it too?' he asked gruffly.

She nodded, her throat tight with emotion, her eyes blind with tears. At this precise moment nothing else mattered.

'I knew it hadn't died for you, I knew you were fighting yourself, not me.'

He was so familiar, so achingly familiar. She knew every inch of this man, and she wanted him with a depth of feeling that was truly amazing considering all that had happened. She began feverishly unbuttoning his shirt, searching out the silken-smooth hardness of his skin long before he had shrugged it off his shoulders.

Now her breasts were crushed against his bare, hair-roughened chest and their mouths clung together yet again. It was like drinking pure nectar. Her heart drummed painfully and every one of her pulses made themselves felt.

She urged her body close to his, felt his unashamed response—and knew in that instant that she was making a terrible mistake. If she didn't stop now it would be too late—if it wasn't already! It was only the sane part of her mind that was telling her to stop, everything else wanted and needed and ached and responded.

Her body tensed without her realising it and Drake raised his head to look at her questioningly. 'Is something wrong?'

'*This* is wrong—you and me doing this,' she told him huskily. 'I——' And then she knew what she had to say. The one thing guaranteed to stop her husband dead in his tracks. It wasn't how she'd meant to broach the subject, but it seemed at this moment the right thing to say. 'I—I'm no longer on the Pill, Drake. We must stop now before we lose control. I know how you feel about children, and we daren't take the risk.'

'I was wrong, totally wrong,' he said hoarsely. 'I let my childhood affect my judgement. It was the worst mistake I could have made.'

It was an amazing admission, and Sapphire could not believe she was hearing him correctly. Her heart actually stopped beating as she waited for him to go on.

'I've thought long and hard about this, Sapphire; I want us to have children—I truly do. I want a family, I want at least two, maybe three. I know you'd never turn your back on them the way my mother did me.' With a groan Drake captured her mouth again, giving her no chance to voice her astonishment, and this time there was no gentleness, this time he ravaged her senses, demanding and taking until every part of her responded with equal passion. There would be time to talk later, time to wonder and marvel over this unexpected change of heart.

His hands slid possessively over her body, moulding and shaping her to him, impatiently disposing of her briefs, exploring, touching, exciting, and when he discovered the depths of her arousal he drew in a swift, sharp breath of pleasure and began to wriggle out of his trousers.

Then just as he lay down beside her the doorbell rang. He went tense and muttered, 'Let's not answer it. Whoever it is will go away.' But whoever it was had no intention of leaving. The bell rang repeatedly until in the end Drake bounced to his feet, swearing angrily as he pulled on his trousers and shirt. 'Dammit, can't a man get any privacy in his own home? Whatever you do don't go away,' he grated. 'I'll be right back just as soon as I get rid of them.'

But the respite brought Sapphire to her senses, made her realise that letting Drake make love to her was still not the right thing to do, even after his surprising and exciting admission. It was a step in the right direction, a very big one, a major one in fact, but there were still other areas of their marriage to be sorted out before she could allow such intimacies. The instant he left the room she began to get dressed, and then she heard a female voice, and when she heard that female voice getting nearer, she was very glad she had.

'I hope I've not called at a bad time, Drake?' Caroline's voice was bright and cheerful and faintly possessive, and it was obvious she had walked in without waiting to be invited.

Sapphire gave an inward groan when she realised who their visitor was. She had welcomed the reprieve, but she certainly did not welcome Caroline Brecon.

'Well, actually, yes, you have, Caroline,' Drake told her. 'It would have been much better had you phoned first. Sapphire and I are——'

'Sapphire?' Caroline sounded stunned. 'She's here? You're back together? I had no idea.'

'She's been here over three weeks now,' answered Drake.

'Oh, I see. Well, I'll just say hello and then be on my way.' By this time they had reached the living-room, and Caroline smiled easily. 'Hello, Sapphire. Why didn't you phone me? We could have got together like old times.'

'I've been busy.' Sapphire found it difficult to sound pleased, when Caroline had come calling on Drake and not her.

'The photography club are justifiably proud of you, Sapphire. You must come and tell us all about your success some time.'

Sapphire shook her head. 'I don't think so. I'm not into giving lectures and that sort of thing.'

'When she's not busy with her photography she's busy with me,' announced Drake with a satisfied smile. 'Aren't you, my sweet?' He put his arm about Sapphire's shoulders and held her close, and Caroline ought to have taken the hint, but she either deliberately ignored it or was amazingly obtuse.

'Would you like a cup of tea?' asked Sapphire when a sudden silence made her feel uncomfortable. Not that she wanted to encourage Caroline, but short of telling her to get out she had no option but to be sociable. Perhaps the girl would refuse.

Caroline did no such thing. 'That would be lovely,' she said. 'I'm dying of thirst.'

'I'll make it,' said Drake at once, 'while you two catch up on the latest gossip.'

Caroline's disappointment showed, and when he headed off towards the kitchen she said to Sapphire, 'Do you really think you'll make a go of it this time?'

'I'm sure of it,' Sapphire answered, injecting a much more positive note into her voice than she felt. 'We're both a great deal wiser.'

'He's not working the long hours he used to?' Caroline's blue eyes wandered in the direction of the kitchen.

'Not at all.'

'You don't think he'll go back to it after a while? And you don't think he's still—er—seeing this other woman?'

Sapphire had no idea, it was one of the things that she needed to clear up before they could resume any sort of relationship, but she had no intention of letting Caroline know this. 'Of course he isn't.' And she mentally crossed her fingers that it was true.

'I know how unhappy you were before; for your sake I hope he isn't.'

The girl sounded sincere, and yet Sapphire knew she had her eye on Drake herself, knew she wanted to split them up again so that she could get her nails into him. 'It's all in the past,' she said cheerfully and firmly. 'We've resolved our differences. I can foresee a long and happy life together.' Or a stormy life, or no life at all!

Caroline did not quite hide the disappointment in her eyes, and after a moment she got up and said, 'I've suddenly remembered something; I haven't time for that tea after all. Give Drake my apologies, will you?' And she whirled on her heel and marched out of the room.

Politeness made Sapphire follow and let her out of the house. 'I'm sorry you have to rush off like this, Caroline. Perhaps another time you'll stay and have tea with us?' She put deliberate emphasis on the word *us*.

Caroline gave an unconvincing smile and a nod as she climbed into her car, starting the engine and driving off so fiercely that the wheels spun.

Sapphire smiled to herself as she walked back into the house. 'What's happened to Caroline?' asked Drake, looking surprised.

'She remembered another engagement,' Sapphire told him with some satisfaction. 'I think she was disappointed you weren't alone. I can't believe you let her walk in when you knew I was lying naked on the sofa.'

He shrugged. 'I didn't have much choice—she's one very determined lady. What made you get dressed? Did you hear her coming?'

'Because I changed my mind about what we were doing.' There was a sudden, sharp edge to her tone that made him frown. 'Letting you make love to me will solve nothing at all. I have to reach a decision in my own way.'

'Damn you, Sapphire,' he grated, 'what the hell do you mean by that? What sort of a decision? I've tried my hardest to make this marriage work; what else do I have to do to convince you?'

Convince her of what? That he loved her? Why couldn't he come out with it? Why did he leave this doubt in her mind all the time? She looked at him stonily. 'There's still the question of your—affair. Am I supposed to ignore it?' she asked, her tone sharp. 'Am I supposed to forgive you your infidelity, push it to the back of my mind and pretend it never happened? Am I to get no explanation, no apologies, no assurance that it won't happen again? I get the impression that all you're interested in is my body—or any woman's body, come to that. Feelings and emotions aren't a part of your make-up.'

'Any woman? You wouldn't be thinking of Caroline, by any chance?' His tone was equally harsh, a frown deepening and darkening his brow.

'She did come here to see you.' Sapphire eyed him steadfastly. 'Who's to know how many other times she's been while I'm out taking photographs?'

'When you're out I'm out, when you're in I'm in,' he stated savagely. 'It's as simple as that. Caroline has taken a fancy to me, I freely admit it, but I've never encouraged her. You have nothing to worry about in that direction.'

Sapphire lifted her shoulders in reluctant acceptance. 'OK, but how about the woman you were seen with in London?'

'I wondered when we'd get back to that,' he said with a grim twist to his mouth. 'If it's a time for truths then I'll tell you. It was my mother.'

'Marie?' asked Sapphire with a frown.

'No, not Marie—of course not. My real mother.' There was no pleasure in his voice as he spoke.

She stared at him in astonishment. 'I didn't know you were seeing her. I didn't know you even knew where she lived.' He had always sworn he wanted nothing to do with her.

'I don't. I bumped into her quite by accident—at least, I think it was accidental; knowing my mother, I can't be sure. She's still as glamorous as ever, still single, doesn't look a year older than I remembered.'

'And are you still seeing her?'

'Heavens no!' he exclaimed. 'We had lunch together a few times—I felt that perhaps I ought to give her another chance, after all, she did bring me into the world, there had to be some tie between us, but it didn't work out. The fact is she'd heard how well I was doing and thought she'd try to cash in on it.'

'She asked you for money?' Sapphire enquired huskily.

He nodded.

'And did you give her any?'

He sat for a moment saying nothing. 'I thought about it, I thought about it a lot, but apart from giving birth to me she gave me precious little else. So I decided that when she left me with Eric she'd severed all connections. I said no. It was a hard decision, but I knew that once I started it would never end, and I have no wish to support her and her steady stream of boyfriends.'

Sapphire did not know what to say. It was a confession she had not expected; she had never dreamt the woman Caroline had seen him with was his mother.

'You're as dumbstruck as I was?'

She nodded. 'It's unbelievable.'

'I know; it made me feel quite sick that she could be so mercenary. I didn't want to tell you, it's not something I'm particularly proud of, but you needed to know so that you could put your mind straight that there's no other woman in my life. There never has been, Sapphire, there never will be.'

'How about the woman you took on holiday? Are you suggesting that she was your mother as well?' There was sharp accusation in her voice and her eyes were cold as they met his.

Drake looked startled and a deep, sudden frown etched his brow and narrowed his eyes. 'What the hell are you talking about? What holiday?'

'Don't deny it,' she snapped. 'I was worried about you when you didn't come home the day after we'd had that argument, so I rang your office. Hélène was extremely surprised to hear from me, having got the impression that we were away together. I'm afraid she wasn't very diplomatic. You never had time for me, Drake—what had this woman got that I hadn't?'

'Hélène didn't say anything to me about you ringing.' He did not answer her question, looking totally stunned instead.

'Perhaps she was afraid of losing her job because she'd put her foot in it, so to speak,' said Sapphire caustically, 'although she must have known I'd confront you with it at some time or other. Anyway, as far as I was concerned the damage was done. Coming on top of everything else it was the last straw.'

'Why the hell have you said nothing about it before?' he demanded. 'My God, if this is the real reason you walked out then why didn't you tell me? Why did you let me go on thinking it was just because of the hours I worked?'

'It was both.' And he wasn't denying it! She felt close to tears. Always she had hoped it had been a mistake, although it was difficult to see how; Drake's PA was the one person guaranteed to know his every move. 'Can you imagine how I felt, knowing you'd gone away, when it was more than you could do to take even a weekend off with me? I was devastated, Drake.' And then, in a tiny little voice, entirely unlike her usual well-modulated tones, 'Are you still seeing her?'

'Sapphire, Sapphire, there's no one, there never has been anyone else but you.' He took her by the shoulders and looked deeply into the navy blue of her eyes. 'I did go away, yes, and I told Hélène I was taking a holiday—she obviously assumed I meant together—but I only stayed one night. I spent the whole time thinking. We were drifting further and further apart, and I couldn't handle it. When you threatened to leave me I was distraught, I blamed myself completely, but I didn't know what to do. I couldn't promise you a nine-to-five job, not at that stage, but I knew that if I didn't do something I'd lose you—and that was the last thing I wanted.'

Feeling as though a weight had been lifted from her shoulders, Sapphire looked at him, smiling cautiously. 'Is this really true?'

'My darling, yes, oh, yes. I thought long and hard right through the night and all the next day; in the end I decided you meant more to me than my business. But in my damned hurry to get back home I slipped down the hotel stairs and ended up in hospital with a broken leg.'

Sapphire gasped and felt the blood drain out of her face. This was certainly something she hadn't anticipated. 'Drake, I'm sorry—I had no idea.' She felt sick inside that this had happened to him without her knowledge.

'When you never answered the telephone I kept imagining you were out with that bastard Colin. In the end I discharged myself, and what did I find? An empty house, all your clothes gone, nothing at all to remind me of you. It was as though you'd never existed.

'Oh, Drake!' Sapphire touched her fingers to his lips. Whereas earlier she would have said it served him right, now she felt nothing but remorse.

'I tried Colin, but he knew nothing; I rang your mother, not letting on that you were missing—I didn't want to alarm her. When I drew a blank I think I went berserk. I took a bottle of whisky to bed, and that, combined with the medication I'd been taking, knocked me out. Time lost all meaning. The phone rang a few times, but it was never you, so I stopped answering it.'

'How long did you go on like that?' asked Sapphire in a hushed voice. This was terrible. It was all her fault. She ought to have been more understanding as far as Drake's work was concerned, she ought never to have threatened to leave him, she ought to have been there when he needed her. She forgot her own suffering, she forgot everything except that she had let Drake down.

'I don't know; days, weeks—yes, weeks, I think. When I began to feel better I felt angry rather than worried. You hadn't left a note. You'd walked out on two years of marriage without a word. I decided that when I caught up with you I'd make you pay for it.'

Sapphire chewed her bottom lip. 'Drake, I'm so sorry, but I was hurt too, you know. You didn't seem to be making any effort to save our marriage. I could see it going downhill, and yet you were planning to spend even more time away from home. After that last argument, when you didn't even sleep with me, and went to work without saying goodbye, I too felt hurt and angry.'

'I guess we've both done a lot of things we regret,' he said sadly. By this time they were sitting on the sofa, his arm about her shoulders, his eyes never once leaving her face. 'I searched for you, Sapphire, I searched high and low—but, hell, living in this out-of-the-way place no one had seen you leave and no one knew anything, not your parents, your sisters, Caroline—no one.

'I swore everyone to secrecy,' she said softly.

He nodded. 'I've realised that since; your damn London subterfuge made me very angry indeed. It was a chance meeting with Louise and our very enlightening conversation that gave me the answer to my problem.'

'Do you still believe I turned up because I needed your money?'

He quickly shook his head. 'That's only one of the many mistakes I've made. I've been a swine to you, Sapphire, I freely admit it. On the other hand, you're not entirely blameless yourself.'

She frowned. 'What am I supposed to have done?'

'I'm talking about Robin, our friendly family man.'

'Drake, that's uncalled-for,' she said crisply. 'As I've told you dozens of times before, Robin is nothing more than a friend.'

'That's the truth?'

She inclined her head. 'The truth.'

'He loves you.'

'Maybe,' she said with a shrug. 'But he never made an issue of it. He always respected my feelings, and they never went beyond the bounds of friendship.'

'Has there been anyone else?' asked Drake.

'No.'

'Not since the day you met me?'

'No one.'

'How about Colin?'

'There was nothing in that either.'

'Then I think that tells us something, don't you?' Although he gave an outward appearance of being totally relaxed a tell-tale muscle still jerked in his jaw.

Sapphire did not answer, but her heart began a crazy rhythm all of its own.

'I think it tells us we're right for each other, that neither of us wants anyone else. Do you agree?'

Slowly Sapphire nodded.

'Then there are no problems, there's nothing else left to sort out.' Drake smiled, as though that was it, as though the whole affair had been cleared. 'I think we can get back down to business, Sapphire.' And so saying, he pulled off his shirt.

CHAPTER TEN

SAPPHIRE did not find it easy saying no to Drake, but somehow she managed it. 'You're asking for sex for the sake of it,' she protested. 'This isn't how it should be at all. I can't just jump back into bed with you.'

He looked as though he could hardly believe what he was hearing. 'Then you tell me how it should be,' he rasped.

'The time still isn't right,' she said. 'I think we need to get to know each other all over again. Too much has happened to just carry on where we left off.'

He shook his head. 'This is bizarre; I don't understand you, Sapphire.' For several long seconds he stood looking at her, warring with her, then with a deeply resigned sigh he muttered harshly. 'You win. We'll begin our courtship all over again.' He turned away from her and stood a moment looking out the window, then he swung around and with a hint of formality, and only the faintest of smiles, said, 'Are you doing anything tonight, Sapphire? If not, will you come out with me?'

Sapphire toyed with the idea of saying she had to wash her hair, but somehow she did not think Drake would appreciate her humour, so she inclined her head gravely. 'That would be very nice, thank you. I accept.'

'Good. Be ready for half-past seven.' And with that he walked out of the room.

Their courtship was a novelty. Drake became an old-world gentleman, very right and proper, doing no more than hold her hand and kiss her chastely on the cheek during their first few 'dates'. It took a long time for their relationship to progress to a proper kiss, and long before then Sapphire wished she hadn't said anything.

She was filled with passionate longing all the time they were together, her body craving his with a terrible hunger. She knew that all she had to do was give in, show him that she desperately needed to be loved, but pride forbade her, and so their affair continued to develop slowly and painfully.

The worst part was lying in bed at night wishing he was with her. Her need of him grew worse with every minute and hour that passed, and she guessed Drake felt the same. He was an extremely virile man, and making love had always come high on his list of priorities. She had never questioned it in the beginning; it was only lately that she had begun to wonder whether this was all he wanted her for. He had still not uttered one word of love, and before she could give in to him she needed to know how he felt. It was no good resuming married life only to find that his feelings for her were not and never had been as strong as her own.

When he said one day that they were going away for the weekend she looked at him in surprise, and her heart began to beat dangerously fast. Was this it? Was he playing the drama out to the full? She dared not ask; she did not want to spoil his game, but she packed her sexiest nightdress just in case. She knew the time was fast approaching when she could hold him off no longer.

She had no idea where they were going when they set off early on Saturday morning, but after an hour or two's driving, through Exeter and Salisbury and still heading east, finally joining the M3 motorway, she knew they were going to London. An excellent choice, she thought. Whereas most people got away from the city for their weekend breaks, to her it was a welcome change.

They weren't silent, they talked throughout most of the journey, but it was about things of absolutely no personal interest—world affairs, books, objects of interest that they passed, anything except themselves.

Nevertheless, Drake was warm and friendly, smiling at her often, letting her see his interest in her, as any man would a new girlfriend. It was a unique experience, a backwards step in their relationship, and yet Sapphire felt that it was working, that forcing Drake to woo her all over again was having the desired result.

But when he pulled up outside a block of luxury flats not far from Greenwich, flats which had been converted from an old warehouse and overlooked the Thames, she could not believe he was doing this to her. 'We're staying with your parents?' she asked incredulously, feeling her heart plummet downwards. This wasn't what she had envisaged.

'Doesn't a guy usually take his girl home to Mother when he's serious about her?'

Sapphire's mouth fell open and she shook her head. 'I don't believe this. You're playing the game too far.'

'It's your game,' Drake said crisply, then added, his whole face suddenly taut with suppressed anger, 'Dammit, Sapphire, I've had about as much as I can take. I can't live in the house with you and not touch you, not make love to you. It's safer here, otherwise there's a strong danger you might accuse me of rape.' He got out before she could respond, and when Marie and Eric appeared in the doorway of their ground-floor flat, warm, welcoming smiles on their faces, it was too late to say anything.

'This is wonderful,' said Marie enthusiastically. 'My two favourite people for the whole weekend. I was thrilled to bits when you phoned, Drake, and announced that you were coming.' She hugged them each in turn and led the way through their sitting-room to the little terrace overlooking the clean flowing water of the river. Terracotta tubs were filled to overflowing with geraniums and fuchsias, petunias and marigolds and blue and purple clouds of trailing lobelia.

After she had seated them both, fussing like a mother hen, tucking a cushion behind Sapphire and making sure she was comfortable, Marie said, 'Lunch will be about fifteen minutes. I expect you're starving? And if I know Drake he hasn't even stopped for a cup of tea on the way.'

Sapphire shook her head.

'The kettle's boiled—Eric's making it,' she said, and as if on cue the older man walked into the living-room bearing a tray holding a beautiful Victorian silver tea-service. Marie carefully poured the tea into wafer-thin china cups with a wild rose pattern on them. 'This is lovely, having my family around me,' she beamed. 'We've missed not seeing you, Sapphire—haven't we, Eric?'

Her husband nodded. 'More than words can say.' And his eyes were kind as he looked at the young girl.

They both loved her, these two people, she thought. She had hurt them badly when she walked out on their son, so badly that Marie had suffered a heart attack. Whenever she thought about it Sapphire went cold inside and vowed she would never willingly do anything to hurt this woman again. Except that she could not take up her relationship with Drake just to please his mother! She needed to be very sure that he loved her.

Lunch was a pleasant, informal meal, and afterwards they strolled along the riverbank talking desultorily about all manner of things. The day passed extremely quickly and peacefully, except when Sapphire caught Drake's eyes on her, which was often, and her heart beat its own military tattoo within her breast. He had said they were here because he could not bear to be alone with her, and yet he was still making it absolutely clear that he desired her. *Desire* being the operative word, she thought sadly.

The evening was warm and balmy, and long after their supper they sat outside sipping wine and talking and generally enjoying each other's company. Eventually, though, Drake yawned and said he thought it was time they went to bed. Eric said he was going to have an early night too, but Marie stayed downstairs to read her book.

Sapphire had been wondering about their sleeping arrangements, and her fears were realised when she discovered that Marie had put them both in the same room.

'I couldn't tell my mother we're not sleeping together,' said Drake when he saw her anxious face. 'It would worry her to death.'

'So what are we going to do?' she asked sharply. The room was *en-suite*, but it wasn't large enough to accommodate any easy-chairs or a sofa. There was nothing but the central, comfortable-looking bed with its peach and cream duvet which matched the curtains.

'It looks as if we have no choice,' he said, trying his hardest to control a smile which insisted on turning up the corners of his mouth. 'I shouldn't worry about it. It won't be the first time you've slept with me.'

'But I thought you said this whole weekend was so that you wouldn't feel the strain of being close to me?' The situation here was actually worse than at Treetops. At least there they had separate rooms; here there was no hope of avoiding each other.

Although Sapphire had initially thought Drake was taking her to a hotel, and had even faintly looked forward to it, all that was forgotten. He must have known this would happen. Contrary to his statement that they would be safer here than at home, it had been his devious way of getting her into bed with him. Her fury boiled over, her eyes brilliant with anger, but before she could speak Drake said:

'Don't worry, I won't touch you unless you want me to.'

'You're damn right you won't touch me,' she snapped, 'I'll make sure of that. You're a devious swine, Drake Rivelin, and I don't know why I ever let you drag me back to Treetops.' She snatched her nightdress from her bag and slammed her way into the bathroom, taking her time as she showered, fuming silently. Although she wanted to rant and rave at Drake she knew she must keep silent for Marie's benefit. She did not want the older woman to hear them and get upset. Perhaps that had been in his mind too. My God, she thought, what sort of a man was it that she had married?

As she pulled on her diaphanous cream nightdress and re-entered the bedroom she wished she had brought a sensible cotton one with her. This had been a crazy mistake and Drake would certainly see it as an invitation.

He sat on the bed waiting for his turn to use the bathroom. She had been hoping to dive straight beneath the sheets before he noticed what she was wearing. It was a faint hope. His eyes narrowed and he slowly looked her up and down, missing nothing. When he spoke his voice was gruff with emotion. 'You're hardly playing fair,' he said.

This was not the reaction Sapphire had expected, and she frowned faintly. 'What do you mean?'

'How am I supposed to ignore you when you're dressed like that? I'm not made of stone, Sapphire. As Oscar Wilde once said, "I can resist everything except temptation".' He paused a moment, then went on, 'Or does it perhaps tell me something about the sort of weekend *you* were expecting? Is that it? Despite your show of outrage perhaps you actually want me to make love to you?' And when she still did not answer, 'Dammit, Sapphire, get into bed. And if you know what's good for you you'll be asleep when I come back.' He crossed the room and yanked open the door.

'Where are you going?' She somehow managed to find her voice.

'For some fresh air, a walk—I suddenly can't stand the heat in here.'

'But what will Marie think?' Too late he had gone, the door closed behind him and Sapphire was left standing looking at it. She really could not understand her husband. He was not behaving at all in the manner she had expected. Had she truly misjudged him?

She climbed into bed, but knew she would not sleep. How could she, when her body was filled with love? When she ached for him more than she ever had in her life? What would Marie think, though, of him going out like this? What excuse had he made? Perhaps she ought to go down and have a word with her mother-in-law herself, reassure her that there was nothing wrong, declare that it was a normal course of events for Drake to take a walk before bed.

She pulled a matching négligé over her nightdress, and Marie looked up as Sapphire entered the room. 'You're not thinking of following Drake dressed like that?' A mischievous smile accompanied her words and she patted the seat beside her. 'Come and sit down, and in a minute I'll make us both a hot drink.' No questions asked, nothing except acceptance of the situation.

'You're a remarkable woman, Marie,' said Sapphire fondly. 'You must know that Drake and I are still struggling.'

'Of course I know, my dear. No problems are resolved in five minutes, or even five weeks. It'll take a long time, it's like beginning all over again. But I can see the effort you're both making, and I have every confidence that all will work out well in the end.'

'We've been sleeping in separate bedrooms,' said Sapphire.

'Oh, dear.' Marie grimaced, but she did not look unduly upset by the confession. 'I've messed it all up, have I? There is another bedroom, but it's very tiny, and actually it's full of junk. Is it too great a problem? Is that why Drake's gone out?'

'Sort of,' admitted Sapphire, 'and I didn't help matters by wearing this nightdress. I'm totally confused, Marie. I don't think Drake loves me, that's the trouble.'

Marie looked at her sharply. 'Not love you? How can you say that? The boy's mad about you—it's as clear as the nose on your face.'

'He's never told me,' said Sapphire huskily.

Marie muttered a few words beneath her breath. 'Some men are like that, Sapphire. They have difficulty in expressing their emotions, but it doesn't mean they don't feel them. Is this one of your problems? Are you still holding him at arm's length until you're sure how he feels?'

Sapphire nodded.

'Have you told him that *you* love *him*?'

'Not since we got back together.'

'It strikes me that you're both creating problems that aren't there. I think you need to sit down and have a good talk.'

'I know,' said Sapphire, 'I keep telling myself that, but I can't just say, "do you love me, Drake?". It has to come spontaneously from him, and since he's not said it once in all the time we've been married, I can't see him doing it now.'

'Who can't you see doing what?' Drake emerged from the shadows, and Sapphire's heart lurched as she looked at the man she loved.

'It was a private conversation,' said Marie pointedly, 'and it's very remiss of you to neglect Sapphire. The poor girl couldn't sleep without you by her side. Away to bed with you both at once.' She squeezed Sapphire's hand tightly. 'Goodnight, my darlings.'

Once in their room Drake looked at Sapphire sharply. 'I hope you haven't been telling tales?'

'Of course not.' Her navy eyes were defensive.

'Then what were you doing talking to my mother?'

'I wanted to reassure her that everything was all right between us,' she said quietly as she climbed into bed. 'The way you stormed off, I knew she must be worried.'

'So what excuse did you give?' he snarled.

'Do you want the truth?'

'Naturally.' There was a slight tensing to his body which Sapphire wouldn't have noticed had she not been watching him very closely.

'I told her the problem was we'd been sleeping in separate rooms.'

'You did what?' The words jerked out of him and he bounced across the room. 'What the hell did you tell her that for? You know I don't want her upset.'

Sapphire shook her head. 'She wasn't upset, she seemed to understand. I think you're trying to protect her too much.'

'And now she knows we're no nearer a reconciliation than we were the day I took you back home. Thanks a lot, Sapphire, you've really done wonders for my manhood.'

'I simply told her the truth as I see it.'

'You wouldn't see the truth if it was waved in six-foot-high letters in front of your eyes. My love for you doesn't seem to make a scrap of difference—all you're interested in is your own damn theory that we have to start all over again. Well, I'm past——'

Sapphire wasn't listening. His love for her! *His love*! Had she heard him correctly? Was he saying he loved her? After all this time, was he actually putting it into words? Could he possibly have loved her all along and never said it?

'Are you listening to me?' Drake touched her shoulder and she jerked out of her reverie to find his eyes intent upon hers. 'I don't think you've heard a word I've been saying.'

'I heard you say you loved me.'

'Of course I love you, you silly idiot. I fell in love with you the day I met you.'

'But you've never told me before.'

He frowned questioningly. 'Haven't I? Perhaps not, but you must surely have known. I didn't think I had to put it into words.'

'No, I didn't know,' insisted Sapphire.

'So why did you think I married you?'

She lifted her shoulders. 'I guess that at the time I thought you loved me—it was only afterwards that I began to have doubts. You'd leave me for days and nights on end, and when you came back all you wanted was my body. Can you blame me for thinking it was pure desire that motivated you?'

'My sweet, silly Sapphire,' he sighed, shaking his head. 'How could you possibly doubt my feelings?'

He sounded so offended that she had to smile. 'It was easy, the way you treated me.'

'Is that why you've been holding me off, because you thought I didn't love you?'

She nodded.

'Oh, my darling,' he groaned. 'I love you, I love you, I love you. I always have and I always will, and I promise I'll never neglect you again,' he assured her. His arms were around her, she was pulled into the exciting warmth of his body. 'I learned my lesson the hard way, Sapphire. The six months I spent without you were the worst days of my life. I thought I was going crazy. Oh, sweetheart, I've done so many idiotic things, so many things I'm ashamed of. But never again. I want to make a clean start. I want you to stop playing games. I want you to be my wife in every sense of the word. I want children, a family, I want——' His mouth was on hers and his last words were lost in a long, immensely satisfying kiss.

Sapphire could not believe that all her dreams were coming true. 'You no longer believe I'm after your money?'

He shook his head emphatically. 'No, no, good heavens, no! I must have been an idiot to even think it.'

'I spent your allowance on my mother,' she whispered.

Drake frowned.

'I don't know whether she told you, but she had an operation and needed a nurse when she came home. I paid for a private one. I fully intended putting it back into the account. I didn't want to take anything from you.'

'You must have hated me very much,' he said sadly.

'No.' Sapphire shook her head. 'I've never hated you, Drake. All I've wished is that you were a little more romantic. I wanted more of you than you were prepared to give.'

'You have it all now,' he said softly. 'Mind, body and soul for always.'

'There's still something else I have to tell you.' A painful memory she had pushed out of her mind and steadfastly refused to think about. But it was important.

If they were to make a fresh start there could be no secrets. After all, it concerned him too. If he hadn't changed his mind about children then she might never have told him, but in the circumstances he deserved the truth.

'I lost our baby, Drake.' Sapphire spoke without a moment's pause. She had not intended to blurt it out like this with no warning of what was to come, but now she was glad that the initial confession was made.

A swift frown claimed his brow. 'Our—baby? Our *baby*! What the devil are you talking about?' Anger began to rise inside him, flushing his face and tensing his body. 'What is this, Sapphire, some kind of sick joke? In any case, I thought you always took the Pill?'

'I forgot, just once,' she confessed.

His frown deepened, gouging his forehead, narrowing his eyes. 'So why wasn't I told you were pregnant? Wasn't I important enough in your life to know the truth?'

Sapphire shivered, a cold chill riding right down her spine. 'I didn't know about it myself until several weeks after I'd left you. When I did find out I was at first appalled and then glad that at least I still had a part of you. I still loved you dearly, Drake. Walking out was the hardest thing I've ever done.'

'But you weren't going to tell me?' he asked harshly.

'You always said you didn't want children.' There was a weariness to her tone as she spoke. 'Then I had a miscarriage and—oh, lord, Drake, it was awful! I lost all interest in living. I wanted that baby so much.'

Drake's anger faded and there was nothing but concern on his face, a suspicion of tears in his eyes, and he gathered her to him, holding her tightly as though he never wanted to let her go. 'My poor dear baby, how you've suffered. I should have been at your side, you should never have gone through that alone. You will be able to have other children?' His tone was anxious, and it was impossible to guess that there had been a time when he hadn't wanted a family at all.

Sapphire nodded. 'The doctor said there's no reason why not.'

'Will you ever forgive me?' he asked throatily.

'There's nothing to forgive,' she whispered against his mouth. 'You're already a changed man.'

He heaved a shuddering sigh. 'I took a long hard look at myself; I really was a bastard. How I could put work before you I don't know. I promise you it won't happen again.'

'I love you so much,' she said.

'And I love you.'

'If only you'd told me before.'

'You honestly never knew?'

Sapphire shook her head. 'I'd had such dreams when we first got married—such dreams.'

'Yesterday's dreams,' he murmured. 'I'm going to make sure they come true, Sapphire. All your tomorrows will be full of happiness, I promise. Now can we make love?' He was already stripping off his clothes.

Sapphire smiled softly at her impatient lover. Never would she doubt him again, never would she confuse desire with love. If ever a man had been humbled it was Drake. She actually felt sorry for him, but she would never tell him that. She would love him and they would have babies and he would always be here to look after her.

Yes, yesterday's dreams were definitely about to come true.

Mills & Boon

Next Month's Romances

Each month you can choose from a wide variety of romance with Mills & Boon. Below are the new titles to look out for next month, why not ask either Mills & Boon Reader Service or your Newsagent to reserve you a copy of the titles you want to buy – just tick the titles you would like and either post to Reader Service or take it to any Newsagent and ask them to order your books.

Please save me the following titles:	Please tick	√
PARADISE LOST	Robyn Donald	
SNOWFIRE	Anne Mather	
A GIRL IN A MILLION	Betty Neels	
HOUSE OF GLASS	Michelle Reid	
MASTER OF PASSION	Jacqueline Baird	
DARK SUNLIGHT	Patricia Wilson	
ECHOES OF LOVE	Jeanne Allan	
ALL IT TAKES IS LOVE	Rosemary Hammond	
SATAN'S CONTRACT	Susanne McCarthy	
TOUCHED BY DESIRE	Lynsey Stevens	
COLD FIRE	Helen Brooks	
UNWANTED LEGACY	Rachel Elliot	
DANCING WITH SHADOWS	Rosemary Badger	
HOLD BACK THE DARK	Jane Donnelly	
DRIVEN BY LOVE	Kristy McCallum	
GARDEN OF DESIRE	Laura Martin	

If you would like to order these books in addition to your regular subscription from Mills & Boon Reader Service please send £1.80 per title to: Mills & Boon Reader Service, Freepost, P.O. Box 236, Croydon, Surrey, CR9 9EL, quote your Subscriber No:................................... (If applicable) and complete the name and address details below. Alternatively, these books are available from many local Newsagents including W.H.Smith, J.Menzies, Martins and other paperback stockists from 11th June 1993.

Name:..

Address:..

....Post Code:.........................

To Retailer: If you would like to stock M&B books please contact your regular book/magazine wholesaler for details.

You may be mailed with offers from other reputable companies as a result of this application. If you would rather not take advantage of these opportunities please tick box ☐